DAWN ROBINSON

# Ditch the Midlife Stress From the Inside Out

## It's time to live with more ease

First edition

This book was professionally typeset on Reedsy.
Find out more at reedsy.com

# Contents

# Part 1 : Once Upon a Time

Once upon a time, you struggled with stress. Sometimes, these feelings seemed to take over your life, at other times you managed to feel better, for a while. But always, there was a search to uncover The Answer, to discover how to live with more ease, to find how you could relax and enjoy your life more.

There were days when you felt so frustrated with the circumstances in your life that eventually you tried techniques like meditation and deep breathing. At times, they helped, and other times they didn't and you couldn't understand why everyone else seemed to be coping so well. You started to wonder if there was something wrong, something flawed about you.

If this is you, you're in the right place (and just so that you know, there's nothing wrong with you).

Relax, all is well.

All good stories have a heroine (you), a villain (your stress), and a fairy godmother (ooh that's me) and together we're going to go on a journey of exploration. As in all good stories, by the end, we'll have changed in some way, we'll see something new and fresh about stress, about how to deal with it and what it says about us.

So make sure you're sitting comfortably and let us begin.

# Chapter 1: A Fairy Godmother Wish

**In which we discover why fairy godmother wishes are not required to deal with your stress.**

This is a book about finding midlife stressful because of crazy hormonal changes, bizarre physical symptoms, petulant, teenage children and never-ending work demands.

So if I were your fairy godmother and could grant you one wish to change an aspect of your life that causes you stress what would it be? Would you like me to whisk you away to a new career with less struggle, difficult colleagues and tight deadlines and more smiles, beanbags and delighted clients? Would you ask me to soothe tempers in your household or magic away items from your complicated, never-ending list of chores?

Maybe you would ask me to make a few personality tweaks so you find it easier to laugh off any midlife worries and preoccupations currently causing you stress and angst. Or perhaps you would prefer me to help you sleep more deeply and wake fully refreshed so that the strains of your life simply drift calmly over your head and you are no longer bothered by inexplicable menopausal symptoms.

If you're here reading this, I'm sure in some way shape or form, you're feeling frazzled and have already tried stress management techniques or read books about living a calmer life. Perhaps they promised fantastic-sounding ideas to rid you of your problem forever but you're still struggling and feeling overwhelmed. And maybe you found all those techniques for dealing with and managing stress such as deep breathing or stress balls irrelevant or a waste of time. At the very least they've been extra tasks to slot into a busy day.

So what if I could promise you none of this frantic managing your feelings is actually required? That even (as far as we're aware) fairy godmothers don't exist, neither does stress in quite the way we've been led to believe.

How wonderful would it be if you suddenly discovered that what you assume you knew about the cause of your feelings is a gigantic mistake – a totally innocent one but a misunderstanding all the same? And everything you believe to be true about the nature of stress and your relationship with it can change for the better in an instant. What if stress is so much easier to deal with than we ever thought possible and we've had it wrong all these years? Are you open to this possibility?

This book isn't about rituals and routines to help you manage stress. You're not going to find a list of things to do here – there are no new qualities you need to develop, no tricky techniques to master.

This is about a way of being.

It has a familiar simplicity about it because it's the way we were naturally when we were children before our minds became busy and worry and overthinking took over. It's about taking away things to do with our mind, to explore what's underneath. Until ultimately we discover there is so little for us to do and so much ease and joy on the other side.

The understanding I'm going to share with you in this book may initially seem counter-intuitive. Certainly, at first glance, it's probably all going to seem a little strange. Whether it does or not, it's a way of being in the world which is very different from the way we have been taught. That's not to say it's difficult or complicated. It's actually the reverse, but it may seem to contradict what to this point, you've always known to be true about how life works.

## How to read this book

Over the course of this book, I want to introduce you to some new ideas, concepts and research and your only task is to read without effort. There's no need to take mental notes or try and figure out how this all works in one go. This isn't about absorbing as much new information as you can, making sense of it intellectually or being inspired and then doing nothing differently. You don't even have to agree with what you see here. Just be willing to remain curious and to keep reading.

How often have you learnt something new, realised it has the power to radically improve your life in some way, turn you into a physical goddess, help you create bucket loads of cash or dramatically improve your health? And despite your good intentions, it's promptly forgotten as life carries on as normal. We rarely change simply because we've uncovered new facts and figures.

Information has such a poor track record when it comes to our own personal transformation. If the opposite were true, we'd all be exercising like athletes, eating dainty, perfectly nutritionally balanced meals like celebrity lifestyle gurus and only drinking wine on Saturdays.

Something different is required.

So I'd encourage you to read this book as you might watch waves when you're relaxing on a beach or lying in a meadow gazing at fluffy clouds drifting lazily across the sky. You're just watching lightly, without effort, with nothing particular on your mind, no need to analyse or make rational sense of any of it.

You know how it is when you're away on holiday and all the problems and issues you're caught up with when you're at home simply seem as if they're another world away. Then, as you're relaxing, paddling in the sea, or floating on a blow-up swan in a pool with a drink in your hand, simple ideas for ways to tackle those problems pop suddenly into your mind.

Obviously I can't provide the pool, sunshine, or inflatable swans. But my hope for you whilst reading this book, or later when you're running errands or reclining in a bath, is for you to have flashes of insight or "ah-ha" moments. And to help you explore further, at the end of each chapter there are more questions for you to ponder so you can relate what we're talking about here to your own situation. Then as these insights begin to accumulate you'll notice you're starting to see the world differently.

No effort required.

Your relationship with stress will transform so that change happens easily and effortlessly. New reactions and behaviours will appear - no internal fight between what you want to do and what you know is in your best interests, required. Midlife is no longer a struggle but all the growth, transformation and new opportunities that can so easily be the promise of this time of life are yours.

This is my fairy godmother wish for you.

There's very little to do. Allow me to shower you with fairy insight-dust. Take it gently, read lightly without having to judge, analyse, or compare with what you already know. Just see where your insights lead you and don't take my word for any of this. Use your experience as your own scientific laboratory – play with the ideas, see how they relate to your world and let the magic begin.

**Over to you**

What drew you to this book in the first place?

What are you hoping to discover here?

What fairy godmother wish would really help you right now?

# Chapter 2: Once Upon a Midlife Crisis

**In which I share my own midlife story of struggle and despair and back out the other side to renewed optimism and zest.**

There's no doubt that midlife can create the perfect stress storm. Demands of children, worries about aging parents, menopausal symptoms and our own fears and concerns about getting older can leave us struggling. And of course, let's not forget there may be something non-age specific going on in your life that's causing you stress at the moment.

So what has brought you here?

Are you generally laid back, calm and collected but stressed in some specific area of your life? Are you the sort of person who breezes through multi-tasking, juggling career, family and social life but metamorphoses into Frazzled Banshee whenever you look at your latest bank statement? Or have stress tentacles crept into every area of your life? Is it sustained, relentless pressure over weeks, months that makes you buckle or are you susceptible to the slightest dip and wobble?

Perhaps your stress comes from relationships – ups and downs with a partner, or a bossy work colleague, health niggles or juggling family demands. Maybe you feel weighed down by physical symptoms that have turned up with menopause - mind fog, sudden weight gain, difficulties sleeping. It can seem at times as if there are an unending number of issues that can potentially cause our stress.

Certainly, since my early thirties, anyone looking in on my life might have assumed it's been relatively easy for me. But every so often because of my fundamentally neurotic and worried nature, stress in one form or another has jumped back up to hit me over the head - I've definitely had my ups and downs.

Over the years I've been anxious or alarmed at one point or other by;

- Money – stress about what to do when there doesn't seem to be enough, how to cope with the latest bill that's popped up out of nowhere and occasionally (very occasionally) how to look after what I do have sensibly.
- House calamities – buying properties when prices are escalating fast, selling during property crashes and peace-of-mind-destroying ginormous repair bills.
- Health concerns especially strokes, high blood pressure, low blood pressure (and any type of blood pressure in between), multiple sclerosis and brain tumours.
- Worrying about my husband getting stressed and the impact on his health.
- Meteorites wiping out civilization, sinkholes, new plagues, global warming, supervolcanoes, nanotechnology, religious extremists and being in a plane that's about to crash.
- Being hit by lightning whilst out walking on exposed and high footpaths (if you ever come across middle-aged woman shuffling

9

along in a very hunched position it could be me).
- Finally and more insidiously, fretting about not being stressed when I suddenly realise I'm taking life a little too easy and that's always a sure sign that something else is going to go wrong.

I'm sure if I was able to ask, you'd have a similarly lengthy and varied list.

For large swathes of my life though, money has sat right up at the top of my list of struggles and stresses – we've had what can only be described as a tricky relationship.

My investments have had an annoying habit of shrinking with unexpected economic downturns. Buying somewhere to live has invariably coincided with property slumps and negative equity and sudden windfalls have spontaneously coincided with equally unanticipated bills.

Intimidating bailiffs have thumped aggressively at my door and trotted off with every possession I love. I've been homeless and destitute. Thankfully, these last distressing examples have only ever existed in my imagination, usually at some unearthly time of the morning. They were the product of an anxious mind and a tendency for overthinking. But I can assure you, like your stress or that of the person next door, the suffering these fears and worries caused was real enough.

I am very aware that my financial stress has only ever been of the comfortably well-off kind. Whenever I have truly needed financial help, it's been there and I've always managed to evade complete money meltdown. I know how lucky this makes me. Fortunately, I've never reached rock-bottom and have always had enough money to pay for somewhere to live, enough to eat, heat my home and cover bills. Through it all, I've been able to keep my head above water. I know how impossible this is for so many people and you could argue with justification that I have never been subjected to real hardship. But in my mind, money has still given me more than a few nightmares.

My struggles with money came to a head when we moved into what seemed like our dream home in November of 2012. I'd fantasised about living in an old house for many years. So when we finally found our home, in a delightful little English village, with school, pub and church, I was thrilled. The quirky cottage was over a couple of hundred years old. It had a large garden with an apple tree, numerous period features and had been renovated by a "professional developer".

Very quickly, the dream fell apart, literally.

A few months later, I took a closer look at deep cracks that had appeared in the sloping ceiling above my five-year-old daughter's bed. I was so concerned, my husband helped me move the bed to the other side of the room and unconvinced, offered to sleep there overnight, whilst our daughter slept with me.

Very early the next morning, I was abruptly woken by the sound of an almighty crash and startled swearing from my husband as a six-foot block of the ceiling collapsed onto the spot where my daughter's bed would have been. As we later discovered, this wasn't just lightweight plaster. The developer had used sticky but heavy cement to try and replicate the old fashioned method of building with lathe and plaster and cement weighing more than four hundred pounds had landed where my daughter's bed had been.

The thought of how my daughter might have fared had she been sleeping below the ceiling when it fell, still leaves me cold. Thankfully, no one was hurt. Despite our best efforts, we had no comeback against the "developer" and were faced with huge, eye-watering bills for repairs that emptied our savings and sent us into a financial spin for years. If that had been the only problem with the house, we probably could have dusted ourselves off and shrugged our shoulders but this was the first of many, if not quite so extreme, problems we had with it.

Needless to say, I found this all very stressful and lost many nights' sleep tossing and turning. It was about this time, I hit a midlife low. There seemed to be always something else going wrong with the house and one problem after the next. I started to anticipate problems and fell into a deep, mental spiral wondering what we ought to do.

I began to wake early in that dark, pessimistic time of the night when fears are exaggerated and worries magnified. My mind started to conjure up ever-more outlandish potential disasters, imaging floors collapsing and wondering how we would cope financially if the back wall flew off or high winds uprooted nearby trees and flung them across the roof.

As my imagination raced from one disaster to the next I became more and more exhausted and fearful and anticipated imminent house-related doom and gloom at any moment. Financial ruin lurked around every corner and I began to daydream about living in a yurt. It wasn't a happy time. And if that wasn't enough, at the same time peri-menopausal anxiety and sleep problems hit me with full force.

But as so often happens, it was this trying, tricky time that sent me back on a spiritual, self-help search that had begun in my early twenties and carried on, albeit with gaps for the next few decades. I had studied

Druidism, Witchcraft (the nudity stopped me from actually joining a coven), meditation, shamanism and NLP – the exploration led me into many fields and along numerous paths and all the books and courses helped me in some way. But when I finally came across the understanding I'm introducing you to in this book, I made a huge leap forward in my mental and emotional health and knew my searching was finally over.

It wasn't long before my new found confidence was put to the test because shortly afterward, we experienced further money problems when my husband was out of work for an extended length of time, I reacted very differently to the way I had done before. I was calm and stress-free and it was then I knew that this understanding had withstood the test of a potentially very stressful situation.

Looking back over the years, I realise, I've been very, very fortunate even with money. But as you'll discover in this book, how we feel about our life and our perception of circumstances doesn't necessarily tie-up with reality. Those who seem to have it all, to have nothing to stress and worry over can still find life difficult. The next person whose life is filled with tough, complicated problems that would leave the majority of us reeling, steps lightly, without care through life. As we all know, the objective reality of a situation has absolutely nothing to do with the intensity of stress we feel.

So is there something else going on with how much of a problem stress is for us other than as a direct reaction to what's happening in our life? Is there an explanation for why sometimes life-changing stress that we expect would floor us is dealt with calmly and the everyday challenges of life leave us reeling?

In this book, I'm going to share where stress really comes from and as you'll discover, the apparently wildly different causes of stress turn out to be irrelevant. The cause of stress is always, always the same. Intrigued? Let's explore further.

**Over to you**

What do you think is the cause of stress and overwhelm in your life?

How does my story relate to yours?

# Chapter 3: Witches, Goblins and Scary Monsters

**In which we uncover where our menacing ideas about stress first came from.**

In this chapter, we're going to explore how our modern idea of stress developed and what the term actually means. But before we go any further, we need to make a distinction between the causes and the symptoms of stress. We'll be looking at this later in the book when we consider how to deal with stress and it's a key issue but we need to make sure we clarify what we're talking about right from the start.

When we talk about the causes of stress we are thinking about all those tricky situations and problems we have – work, relationships, money, health, that disrupt our peace of mind and make us feel overwhelmed and swamped. On the other hand, if we think about the symptoms of stress then I'm sure each of us could come up with a long list of the physical and emotional results of stress that we struggle with – loss of appetite, inability to sleep, worry and anxiety, feelings of being out of control. I'm sure you're familiar with a variety of these.

This is where stress management techniques come in – their aim is to help you deal with and manage the symptoms until at some point, you regain the mental resilience to tackle the causes. When you're able to sleep at night, stop your mind racing or calm your breathing, then you have the spare capacity to get out there and find yourself a more supportive partner, a job that celebrates what you're fantastic at rather than what you struggle with or deal assertively with that tricky neighbour.

We will return to this distinction later and it's something for you to keep at the back of your mind whilst you read over the next few chapters but for the time being, let's turn our attention to stress.

**Where do our ideas about stress come from?**

The use of the word "stress" to describe that familiar collection of unpleasant feelings and reactions was first used in the mid-1930s by the Hungarian endocrinologist, Hans Selye. At the time, he was studying the effect of hormones on rats (worked with a few of those in my time as well) but he became intrigued when he noticed the symptoms of illness they developed were the same, irrespective of which hormone was used. When Selye took the insightful conceptual leap of realising the cause of sickness was the trauma of being involved in the experiment rather than the injected substance, our modern preoccupation with stress was born.

Selye also remembered a number of patients he had seen years before when he worked as a physician whose symptoms such as loss of appetite and a lack of interest in life never seemed to be directly related to their diagnosis. It was as if their body and mind had been ground down by life and he suddenly had a flash of insight that this deterioration in both patient and rat looked very similar.

At this point, it seemed to make sense to Selye to extrapolate his findings from rats to humans believing what was true for rat subjects in lab conditions must also be relevant for humans living in more free-range conditions. He concluded that both humans and rats were suffering from the same disease. These days, more rigorous exploration is required before using the results of animals in a laboratory to provide an explanation for the complexities of human issues and problems. But at the time, it was this work that began the association between stress and ill health.

## What is stress?

All well and good so far, you might argue, but what's come to be seen as a major issue with Selye's work is that he took the decision to define stress as the body's response to anything that places a demand on it, in other words, life. So the term "stress" has come to cover such a range of different reactions that pinning it down is like catching leaves in a hurricane.

Sometimes we use it to describe feelings of deep despair after losing someone we love, on other occasions our mild irritation at having to clear up the kitchen (again). We use stress to encompass both our reaction to chronic, long-term pain and a fleeting argument in a morning meeting with our boss.

What is clear, however, is that we frequently treat stress as if it were an object; something that can be held and tossed around like a bouncy ball from one person to the next. Let's imagine for a moment, we're having a cosy coffee and chat together. I'm sure we wouldn't have too many difficulties agreeing on the characteristics of the cups we were drinking from. They have a physical nature. They're tangible objects with shape and texture, colour and weight in a way that stress as a concept, isn't.

Stress is something we construct in the privacy of our own minds and we all have a very individual representation of what it is and what it feels like. It's a mental construct, a concept we develop and attach meaning to in our heads. This means it's not subject to the same laws as physical objects. A cup never spontaneously turns into a kettle or changes colour. But ideas are fluid and have the potential to transform into something else without difficulty, at speed. They are flexible, transient beings.

That's not to say stress doesn't cause real suffering or that our mental, emotional and physical anguish is purely our imagination. That's definitely not what I'm suggesting and those feelings of stress are very real. But it isn't the concrete entity the articles in magazines - Ten Ways to Combat Stress and Forty-Five Methods for Stress Management would have us believe.

What stress means to us as a concept is created out of ideas and images in our heads like "freedom" or "adventurous". How we think about it and what it means to us can change dramatically over time and from person to person in a way that having a different idea about the cups we're using never transforms their physical reality. We're not talking about a solid, permanent, touch-it-its-real, solid entity here.

Michael Neill, a writer and coach whose work I love, uses the germ analogy to explain how we see stress. This means stress is infectious and can be passed from person to person – if you're working with someone who's stressed, there's a huge risk you're going to catch the stress bug too. Like the equivalent of the bug-ridden swamp, there are places where hordes of stress germs lurk ready and waiting to latch onto you (like a high-pressure job).

If on the other hand, you're sitting in a beautiful garden with a long drink in your hand, there are few and your risk of catching them is very low. When we're with someone who's stressed or we're in one of these high-stress areas, it's usually a good idea to make sure we have regular shots in the arm of antibiotics for stress and that's why we think stress management techniques work. They're providing us with an antidote.

For me, there are always lots of stress germs hiding out at airports, in large crowds or when I'm surrounded by loud music whilst there's virtually none when I'm having a Jane Austen moment - indulging in afternoon tea somewhere refined, perambulating the lanes or spending quiet time with family and friends.

So we have the conclusions from Selye's original work on rats being used to explain stress in humans and this rather all-encompassing definition of stress that could be used to mean any situation we encounter in life. The final factor we need to consider is that much of Selye's later work and many subsequent experiments have involved extreme conditions which are then used to explain stress in the more humdrum day-to-day living most of us experience.

I'm not denying there's evidence this level of physical deprivation and emotional trauma can damage health but thankfully for the majority of us daily stress levels never reach this level of intensity. When we're stuck in a traffic jam or fretting that our work is damaging our health, we can drop our concerns and worries about what this stress is doing to us and get on with living our life because the conditions the rats were subjected to are far beyond the level of trauma most of us will experience. And if we are unlucky enough to find ourselves in stressful circumstances, let's not forget there are many studies that show how our innate resilience enables plenty of people to thrive despite living through harrowing situations.

As Selye himself later admitted, there were flaws in many of his conclusions and by the 1970's he was starting to downplay his earlier results. He'd come to realise that stress can also have a positive impact, that he had jumped to premature conclusions and failed to take into account the inner strength we all possess. But it was too late to turn the tide of opinion that he had helped to create that stress is always a thinly-disguised villain that even in relatively benign situations can cause us to become swamped with short and long term health implications.

So for now, I'd like to leave you with the thought that stress and our reaction to it may be less tangible and concrete than we imagine. It's as if we've woken up in the middle of the night terrified because we're convinced an intruder is in the room. We can hardly breathe with fear only to finally realise with relief, that our potential attacker is a coat hanging on the wardrobe. Our feelings of terror are real enough, our physical reaction isn't made up or imagined but these reactions are based on a misunderstanding, an illusion.

Stress is not a tangible physical reality. It never was although at times we've treated it as if it were. We have ways of thinking about stress that have a huge impact on how and when we experience stress. But it now appears that the underlying foundations that our whole notion of what stress is and how it affects us, was based on flaws right from the very beginning. Our challenge now is to rethink our whole approach to stress because it turns out we may have been looking in the wrong direction all along.

**Over to you**

What's your definition of stress?

What concerns and worries do you have about what stress is doing to you?

# Chapter 4: The Lion, The Witch and The Wardrobe of Stress

**In which we find out more about our common responses to stress.**

Over the years, each of us has come up with our own toolkit of approaches to deal with stress. We may have our personal favourite that we resort to most of the time or we might have a variety of approaches to use and in this chapter, I've outlined what I believe to be the most common.

## 1. Unlock your inner lion

Your first option is to let out a metaphorical roar of defiance and fight it, to stand tall and proud like a lion. You wade in feet first and rush to deal with the causes of your stress, insisting on tackling issues with colleagues head-on or putting yourself on a strict diet and exercise regime to deal with health issues.

You harden your emotions against feeling any symptoms of stress – "toughen up buttercup" as my daughter might say. It becomes a source of pride (excuse the pun) that you can deal with more stress than anyone else. You stiff upper lip it out and laugh in the face of problems. You deny how you feel, brace yourself for a life of struggle and harden your emotions to the difficulties of life. But there is a cost. Life feels hard work, a constant battle and living can be joyless.

## 2. Unleash the witch

The second option you may choose is to manage the symptoms of stress and concern yourself less with tackling the causes. You learn spells and incantations to deal with your physical and emotional reactions and become your own (good), witch. Perhaps you find out more by going on stress management courses or reading piles of books. Maybe you learn to meditate, breathe deeply, or buy squidgy stress balls you can squeeze and pummel when the tension is rising. You accept that life is going to hit you with stress from time to time and that in some way it's going to be a constant in your life.

Every so often you need to retreat to a spa or escape from life to recuperate and to gather your inner resources and strength for the next set of problems. Or you continue on a never-ending search to find the next best way of managing the problem - self-analysis didn't work so perhaps it's time to try meditation. That didn't overcome the feelings of stress so maybe it's time for affirmations and chanting. Your underlying assumption is that if you could *only* learn the correct spell or technique, you would live in a state of eternal calmness and tranquillity despite the chaos in your life.

## 3. Lock yourself away safely in a wardrobe

Finally, you have the option of turning away from stress and doing everything possible in your life to avoid it - metaphorically hiding away in a cosy wardrobe with a good book and a hot water bottle and shutting out the world. This might mean you play small – not taking the job promotion, or starting that new, exciting hobby. You don't do the things that are slightly scary but are going to stretch you.

You lie low.

Every time there's even the smallest chance you're going to feel stressed, you start to distract your mind through habits - drinking, overeating, binge shopping. Or you might back away from situations and relationships you believe are causing you to feel this way. You avoid the pain of stress rather than doing anything to deal with the cause and finding solutions. You limit your life and restrict experiences.

But the problem with this approach is that even when you try and hide, difficult situations are going to find you. As an adult, it's unlikely you've had no experience of stress because life happens and try as we might, there's no way of avoiding problems, trials and tribulations.

**The limitations of these strategies**

Whichever strategy or combination we use, there are risks and problems. For a start, stress is like the relationship I have with my weight as there can be a time lag between our behaviour and the implications of our actions that I often fail to take into account.

More than once, I've eaten a little too much and congratulated myself on miraculously turning into one of those people with a metabolism that enables them to eat anything without putting on weight. Then all of a sudden, literally overnight – all my clothes are too tight. I realise with dismay, I've put on heaps of weight and I'm either going to have to invest in a new wardrobe or my eating habits are going to have to change.

The same can happen to our stress. It can have a habit of creeping up on us, unnoticed and then all of a sudden we've arrived at a crisis point and *everything* becomes the last straw. The slightest upset or problem is enough to make us feel as if we're falling over the edge into the stress abyss.

I'm not going to lie to you. All of these strategies I've outlined for dealing with stress, whether we tackle the causes or simply try to manage the symptoms, work in a limited way.

But in a sense, they're like building a tall tower to keep you safe from monsters. The problem is, it's going to take a lot of work to maintain this anti-stress monster building. You're going to have to keep repairing and always going to have to keep a lookout in case the monster lands on the roof. And then one day you might even discover that the reason you were building the tower to protect yourself never existed in the first place. You might realise that the monsters were simply clouds passing overhead.

That's one of the reasons why stress management techniques don't work – it's as if we're on a constant treadmill. You have to work harder and harder to keep the stress at bay and you need to stay vigilant to make sure stress isn't creeping in. It's exhausting and time-consuming. And whilst all that's going on, your preoccupation with stress management techniques is stoking the fire and keeping the very beast you're trying to rid yourself of, alive.

If these strategies worked, we'd all use them and then hey presto, we wouldn't have to be concerned or worried about stress again because we'd be leading calm, peaceful lives.

So what's required instead?

Well, it's time to go back to the beginning. It's time to question the way in which we view stress, to uncover its true cause and that's what we're going to be looking at in the second part of this book. Then we have the potential not only to manage stress but to change our relationship with it, forever. And therein lies the potential for our greatest transformation.

**Over to you**

How do you typically try to deal with stress in your life?

Do you try and sort out the causes of stress or concentrate on managing your symptoms?

How effectively are these strategies and techniques working for you?

# Chapter 5: You're Already the Heroine of Your Story

**In which we see how being stressed never means there's anything wrong with us.**

"Everyone is sitting in the middle of mental health, they just don't know it."
Sydney Banks

Many stress management approaches start from the assumption that if we're struggling with stress and overwhelm, there's something wrong with us that needs fixing. But before we spend more time together exploring the nature of stress, I'd like to make one point very clear: when we're stressed and finding life difficult, it's easy to fall into the trap of believing it's something about us at fault.

We look around and assume that everyone else is able to breeze through the changes and challenges of midlife without care. Wherever we look there are women our age starting six-figure businesses, completing arduous physical challenges, or looking stunning at Hollywood award ceremonies. We're barely able to get beyond struggling out of our pyjamas and lifting the fifth piece of thickly buttered toast to our lips.

It's too easy to see our lack of apparent success and emotional ease as a flaw in our character, an occupational hazard of having the personality we were unlucky to have been born with. And it means we're never going to cope with the stresses and strains of everyday life because we're the sort of person who's always going to struggle and quite frankly, is never going to get it together.

Or maybe we fear we're damaged by some long-ago incident that's wormed its way unnoticed and forgotten into our psyche or a specific incident that we wish we could forget. We convince ourselves that if *only* we could learn another skill or technique then we'd be able to handle this stress better.

One way or another, we put these uncomfortable feelings of stress and pressure down to a whopping great sign there's something missing in us or something wrong. So not only do we have to deal with the stress of the person, situation, event that's freaking us out but we have to deal with thoughts about how we're dealing with it - layer, upon layer of thinking that destroys our peace of mind, undermines our confidence and sucks all joy from life.

Please don't entertain these thoughts or get bogged down with this thinking. I'm here to tell you there is absolutely nothing wrong with you. It's time to see yourself as the heroine of your story rather than the light entertainment, the evil villainess, or the one who can be relied upon to make a mess of it all.

We all experience moods and sometimes behave badly. We frequently make poor choices and could make better decisions. There are times when all of us struggle and feel we're going to collapse under the weight and strain of bucket loads of stress: when we pray for the world, life, the universe to send us just one teeny, tiny, break, for once. Please!

I fell into this myself for decades. I searched continuously, endlessly for the latest self-help book or technique that could help me. I wanted to skip lightly through life rather than constantly fighting myself, taking one step forward and then several backwards. I felt endless frustration about how I was taking life so seriously, allowing myself to be crushed by the smallest stress and strain.

But as I discovered and I hope you come to see, this stress doesn't mean anything about you. There's nothing wrong with you. You don't need fixing, you're not damaged and you're not broken. All you're suffering from is a misunderstanding, a trick of the mind and once you see what's really going on, you'll relax into living differently.

For the time being, you may need to take this on trust. But I promise you, you have within you all the resilience you need to deal with any stressful situation that seems to be bashing you over the head at the moment. You've already got all the creativity to come up with solutions and new ideas that will help you tackle whatever it is that you are struggling with.

Grappling with stress never interferes with our innate capacity for mental and emotional health and wellbeing. At any moment, no matter our current level of joy or despair we always have the potential for new thought, different ways of being and a never-ending supply of creativity and inspiration that can transform us from wobbling disaster to self-assured, calm superheroine. We don't need techniques to mend anything about us or heal any emotional wound.

This transformation doesn't have to take long. This innate ability is always there for us – there's nothing extra we need to do. All we need to do, all we ever have to do, is to look in a new direction and there it is for us, waiting patiently.

These ideas I'm going to introduce you to form an understanding that is sometimes called a subtractive psychology. It's about stripping back complications and misconceptions to uncover who we really are and how life can work with more simplicity and ease for us once we wake up to this. It's not about adding anything more to who we are and what we have to do to be a success.

Now if you're on medication and going to therapy and it's helping, stay with it. This is not about ditching any lifeline you currently have to health and emotional wellbeing but what you will notice over time is what you need changes. There is never failure in seeking help in whatever form makes the most sense to you at the time.

I suffer from migraines and yes, staying away from red wine, a change in diet, or taking time to relax all help but if I'm suffering an attack, I'm not going to apologise about fumbling around for my packet of tablets, asking everyone to leave me alone and lying down in a darkened room. No self-criticism, no judgment. It just seems to be the action to take and I'll take it until it seems not to be the action to do.

It's that simple.

I want you to trust that if you're here ready to learn more about stress then stress hasn't had the better of you. There's hope, there's always hope and the potential for change is there right up until you take your last breath.

For such a long time I had niggling, wouldn't-leave-me-alone thoughts that I was on the edge of falling deep down into an unhinged state of mind. Outwardly it looked as if all was well. I had a loving family, good friends, work as a management trainer and later as an Alexander Technique teacher that I enjoyed. I held it all together and seemed to cope with life. It looked as if there was nothing wrong. But inwardly I always felt if I could just develop more confidence, a smattering more self-esteem, greater courage, everything would be well.

There's a whole self-help, self-development industry out there promising ten ways to fix this and seventy-five techniques to sort that out and I'm not saying that it can be useful to learn new skills and grow. But this whole premise is built on the presumption that we need fixing, in some way we're flawed. And so consequently I spent decades reading self-help book after self-help book. I'm not knocking it because all of it got me to here, to where I am now and I'm very grateful. But (huge "but" alert) I feel completely differently now.

I'm no longer searching for the latest guru to help me. I'm not constantly knocking myself down in my thoughts, chastising myself for being too wet, too drippy, not dynamic enough, or whatever my latest flavour of self-put-down sounds and feels like. I'm no longer on a constant treadmill trying to improve myself because there was always something else that needed fixing and the list of things I needed to do to maintain this improvement was never-ending and quite frankly, exhausting.

It's like looking from a mountain top at the most magnificent landscape and whining that if a cluster of trees could move slightly to the left and if another mountain range on the horizon were taller, the view would be perfection.

Now, it all seems so absurd.

Since I came across this understanding, I know, deep down, in my heart of hearts, cross my heart and all that, that I'm enough, good enough. The constant search for something to fix me just seems crazy now, like this daft idea of changing an incredible view. I know at a deep level that I've got creativity, resourcefulness, resilience, all of that good stuff already in me and it's become not so much a process of self-development but self-discovery.

There's a very different quality to my exploration now. I'm uncovering more of the talent and ability already buried within me rather than grasping at external qualities and trying to pull them with difficulty towards me. I can enjoy midlife without regrets of the past or fears for the future.

I used to believe my reaction to stress was because I wasn't tough enough or didn't have it in me. Now I recognise all my suffering was because I just didn't understand how life and our minds work not because I couldn't cope with it. I didn't need to work at this. I didn't need to commit to a thirty-day self-improvement campaign with a long list of tasks to do each day. It was more a settling into this awareness that I was enough, not broken, not in need of fixing. It was like allowing my body to sink back, to be supported by the great armchair of life. I didn't need to be in control or keep frantically "doing".

There is nothing wrong with you, whatever your current thinking around that. And all it takes, all it ever takes, is a flash of insight or inspiration and everything can change in an instant. You can have a new, bolder, bigger awareness of yourself in no time at all. A simple misunderstanding can change easily, rapidly with no effort.

And this isn't just me saying this. This understanding has been used for people with traumatic, long-standing problems, for people in prisons and people of every age and creed in countries all over the world.

If you don't believe me, hang on in there. Just be open to the possibility that you are whole and complete. Stay in the conversation and let your innate wellbeing do the rest. Play with the ideas in this book. Entertain possibility and whatever age you are, remember you've already dealt, overcome and managed a hell of a load of stuff already.

So for today, take a moment, breathe deeply, do whatever you need to do with that stressful situation that's in front of you and know, (or just be open to the possibility) that this situation is not showing the world how inept and damaged you are.

You're doing the best you can, with what you have.

All is well.

**Over to you**

Looking back over your life, what struggles and challenges have you been able to overcome?

Where in your life now can you see that you're not broken and you don't need fixing?

# Part 2: Who's Afraid of the Big, Bad, Stress Wolf?

Isn't it strange how we have turned stress into the Big Bad Wolf, a monster to be feared, the villain to be avoided at all costs?

I'd love to promise you're never going to feel stress, anxiety and overwhelm again, that the Big Bad Wolf is going to come to a sticky and permanent end. Wouldn't it be wonderful if we could float our way through life on a happy, hippy cloud of soft colours never touched by pain and struggle?

But that's not how it works.

Unexpected, sudden events always have the potential to trip us up, rip the ground away from under our feet, to have us flailing around. But I promise once you really get this understanding, you'll fall out of stress, far quicker, with more ease, never to fall into the quagmire so deeply again. More importantly, you'll no longer fear it.

This seems to be the way it works.

So in this section, I want to share with you why you don't need to fear stress and how it need become no more annoying than a mild, head cold.

We'll look at research that has the potential to completely transform how you view stress and in the second part of this section, we'll turn our attention to the cause of our stress. These are such important areas to look at because once we understand their role in our feelings of overwhelm, we have the ultimate power and ability to transform our experience of stress and a whole new approach to dealing with the symptoms of stress opens up for us.

# Chapter 6: The Fluffy Lamb in Wolf's Clothing

**In which we learn why stress is not as disastrous for our health as we once thought and how we can use it to our advantage.**

You don't have to look very far to find doom and gloom statistics about the dangers of stress. There are plenty of reports about how it can dramatically reduce the quality and length of our lives, how it's eroding our health, or damaging our mental stability. So in this section, I wanted to share some amazing research that suggests rather than running screaming from the Big Bad Wolf of Stress, we might be better served by learning to see the fluffy, cuddly, lamb beneath the frightening exterior.

The work I'm using here is from the fantastic book "The Upside of Stress." written by health psychologist Kelly McGonigal who works at Stanford in the US. Kelly spent years teaching as many people as she could get her hands on about the harmful effects of stress but in her subsequent Ted talk, she admitted she had changed her mind.

It turns out new research has shown that the harmful effects of stress only exist if you believe stress is harmful. Reality is more subjective than we previously suspected and it's our belief about stress and what it does to our health – body and mind that makes all the difference.

One of the first studies she came across that sowed the seeds of doubt for her involved over 30,000 people in the US. Researchers asked people two questions. Firstly, how much stress they had experienced in the last year and secondly, if they thought stress was harmful to their health? Then these diligent researchers tracked death records for the next eight years to uncover who died and who stayed alive.

As you would expect, the people who reported low stress were fine and the highest death rate was in the group experiencing high levels of stress who believed it was harmful and damaging. They were forty-three percent more likely than average to die over those eight years. But most surprisingly, the healthiest people were those living with high levels of stress who didn't think it was a problem. Typically they felt any feelings of stress helped them deal with challenging circumstances in their lives, giving them mental and emotional resources and the resilience to perform well.

Kelly came to the conclusion that believing stress is bad for you can seriously damage your health whilst working with it as positive energy, is life-enhancing. Stress isn't some monstrous evil creature roaming the streets looking for hapless victims. It's not something we have to tolerate and fight off as best we can as if using a folded umbrella to defend ourselves from a cartoon super-monster.

We have the potential to take an active role in how we respond to it - cowering and quivering, or standing and facing it, it's up to us. But it's a critical decision because the choice we make has a powerful role to play on the impact stress has on our physical and emotional health.

**Beyond the fight or flight response**

You've probably heard about the fight or flight response, our body's response that enables us to fight or run and hide from danger. But just assuming we've only got two ways of responding to stress is too simplistic - researchers have discovered the body is far more sophisticated than this.

The fight or flight response is just *one* way the body can respond to stress. More specifically it happens when we're in self-defense mode because it's a threat response. When this response is triggered, the body is anticipating injury and restricts blood flow and increases blood pressure and inflammation – all designed to limit blood loss and encourage healing which if you've just been hit over the head with a mallet is handy.

These responses are wonderful in the short term and a great response to an immediate problem but if maintained over time, they are the very triggers for health problems like heart disease and chronic inflammation we associate with stress.

**The challenge response**

But think about those times when you're feeling stressed because you need to do well in a job interview or presentation, some form of sport or a time when you simply want to perform to the best of your ability. In situations like these, a little adrenaline and stress can make a world of positive difference. Our mind is sharper, our physical reactions faster and we may even find we're enjoying the very situation we'd dreaded. Our attention is focused completely in the moment and we know exactly what to say and do at precisely the right time.

We feel as if our performance is on fire and there's little effort involved.

This is what's called a challenge response and the body reacts in exactly the same way it does when we're experiencing joy and courage. Blood vessels stay relaxed, the heart pumps faster. Our thinking is clear and our senses sharp.

Both the challenge and threat response have their place although the former is a healthier long-term response to stress. But *how* does the body know which response to use? This is clearly a handy question to know the answer to and I'm not going to keep you in suspense for long! The trigger for which mode is turned on is our perception of our ability to handle whatever is causing our stress.

Let's imagine you're about to be trampled by a hoard of racing buffalo (unlikely to happen I know on the streets of any regular city, but indulge me in this one for a moment). You quickly deduce your chances of being able to get away or outrun this multitude are slim. Body alarm bells are triggered and your threat response is activated, ready to limit the damage as far as possible.

If on the other hand, you have exactly one hour to finish a vital presentation before you stand in front of an important audience but have every confidence in your ability, the challenge response will help you get more done, faster. When you are able to remind yourself how you have handled tricky situations in the past and can become absorbed in the challenge, the task becomes one of experiencing that elusive flow state rather than overwhelm.

As you look back over your life you might also notice how so often it's the difficult times in our lives that turn out in hindsight to be the catalyst for significant personal growth. I know this can be difficult to imagine when you're going through a stressful time and life seems tough but if you reflect on your own experience, you may notice this to be true. It's not until we're tested that we uncover our true strength and resilience. Through times of difficulty, we develop new skills and uncover unknown resources. We find inner strength we had not dreamt for one moment existed.

We amaze ourselves.

I hope this chapter has started you to question any previously held thoughts that stress is harmful to your health and to be avoided at all costs. I'm not suggesting for one moment this means you need to rush out into your life to find more stress to grapple with and if you're having an easy life, you need to start worrying and feeling guilty. But when you are stressed, rather than using avoidance techniques (especially hiding in a large cupboard as suggested in a previous chapter), seeing stress in a very different way is a huge advantage.

We know that what you believe about stress is so important and it's clear that engaging with any stressful situation by encouraging a challenge rather than the threat response can make a big difference. Don't allow yourself to be squashed by stress. You have the ability to deal with what life throws at you and you never know you might even find that stress wolf isn't so scary after all!

**Over to you**

Where has positive stress helped you in your life?

Which difficult times in your life have enabled you to become a stronger person?

# Chapter 7: Falling Down the Rabbit Hole With Alice

**In which we find out why people can feel differently about the same situation and why sometimes we feel stressed when the car breaks down, the kids are rude and the dog is sick. And sometimes we don't.**

**The connection between thoughts and feelings**

In this part of the book, we're going to look more closely at where our stress really comes from (spoiler alert) and this isn't where it seems to come from. And that's strange isn't it because well, stress is just a reaction to circumstances and events that happen, isn't it?

So far we've seen how our experience of stress revolves around a thought. Stress is harmful or not depending on what we believe about it and the body responds to stress as a scary threat or exciting challenge according to what's going on inside our mind.

How incredible is that!

But what if we could dive even further down into the rabbit hole? What if (and obviously this is a completely bonkers idea), what if stress owed its very existence to thought? Let's see where that takes us.

Life makes us stressed.

Other people, problems, too much going on, too little happening, unforeseen events and situations we've long feared, can all lead to stress. Life just keeps on happening to us. Of course, there's room to manoeuvre in how we respond but there's little we can do to stop stress turning up in our life in the first place.

When we're having a rough day, feeling close to the edge of endurance, we might only be capable of putting one foot in front of the other, like fumbling around in the dark, trying to find the light switch. We work on stress damage limitation and simply try and make it unscathed to bedtime. When we're feeling a little stronger and resilient, we've got more energy to deal with the issue that's making us feel stressed and put in one or two solutions to prevent it from happening in the first place.

From a very early age, we're taught that events and situations in our life make us feel a certain way, good, bad, wonderful or indifferent. If the wish genie suddenly popped up in front of us and promised to grant our most precious, dearly held desire, we'd all be ecstatic. Unexpected hate mail from our nearest and dearest would upset even the most hard-hearted of us. Both of these scenarios would produce predictable, universal feelings.

This is so obvious it hardly needs mentioning and the truth of it so deeply ingrained into us that if we each had a "realityonometer" in our core, cut it down the middle and that's what you'd find all the way through. No question about it.

But hang on a moment.

Just because something seems and looks obvious doesn't make it true. This has been evident throughout history. At one time, *everyone* knew the sun rotated around the earth, or that at the edge of the ocean was a giant abyss that sailors feared their ships could fall into.

Then, those outdated, deep-seated beliefs that everyone had happily lived with previously without question, just seemed plain old ridiculous. Of course, *now* we were far wiser and sophisticated, we knew differently because our understanding about the nature of reality had developed and grown.

And so with stress and where it comes from.

If the external world had any power to make us all feel a particular way, happy, sad, relaxed or stressed then that would mean any event would have the same impact on everyone at all times.

Let's take being made redundant for example, sitting right up there near the top of the list of events with the potential to disturb our inner peace, unsettle our sanity and hand us sleepless nights. As far as stress is concerned, it's major. And yet it's perfectly possible for two people to have a completely different experience of sudden unemployment.

Person A, let's call her Chloe, is devastated. She feels a deep sense of failure and torments herself with thoughts of what she should have done to make herself more indispensable to the company. It takes her months to pick up the pieces of her life and start looking for another job. Friends ask how she's doing and she can give a very full and lengthy list of all the aspects of her life that have fallen apart.

Person B (or Amy) feels energised. She feels a deep sense of relief and freedom and expanding opportunities when faced with exactly the same situation and very quickly she's living life more fully than she has done for years. She's vibrant and happy, has quickly found a new job that suits her far better and has discovered a new sense of optimism and excitement about the future.

So it's not that there is anything inherently good or bad about losing a job. How can there be if two people have such completely different reactions?

How about the idea of selling a house and moving home? Again it's up there near the top of stressful events in life. I've lived in about thirty different places in my life and I love moving − I adore the feeling of packing up a house and starting out on the open road, ready for the next adventure. Exploring a new place to live, meeting new people is, in my opinion, the best fun ever. It's exhilarating! And yet I know many other people hate it and consider it inconceivable that anyone would do such a thing voluntarily and vow the only way they'll be moved out of their home is in a box. This is just another example of how the same situations can conjure up opposite reactions in different people.

Even when you think about your own experience, there are some days when you can deal with whatever life throws at you whether it's the car breaking down, the dog being sick, a computer not working (again!). You're able to handle it all with a sense of ease and flow whilst at the same time juggling ten other priorities with no sense of overwhelm. You do whatever needs to be done, with little thought or concern.

Other days, for whatever reason, the day starts badly when you accidentally hit the snooze button on your alarm and fall out of bed in a complete panic about oversleeping. You over-react to each unexpected problem, become flustered when nothing seems to go right and you wonder if you're ever going to cope with any of it again.

Why does this happen?

It's because we're forgetting one vital step between a situation, the "what" that happens to us and our experience, our feelings and then our actions. This vital, often forgotten and neglected step is our thinking and it's only ever possible for us to experience life through our thoughts. When there's no mental processing or awareness, there's no experience, no meaning or interpretation, good or bad and no feelings.

Any circumstance we find ourselves in, every event is neutral but we are meaning creation beings. We attach significance to whatever happens in our life, good, bad, or indifferent because that's what we've learned to do. And we do this through our thoughts. So this is where the "Inside Out" in the title comes from because instead of external situations having the power to make us feel a certain way (outside in), we start to recognise how our experience of life is an inside (going on in our mind) affair.

Let's try a chocolate cake thought experiment for a moment. It has far less calories than consuming the real variety so if you're concerned about calorie intake, you can still take part (and if chocolate isn't your thing, feel free to insert a more compelling substitute).

Imagine the most amazing, gorgeous chocolate cake stood on a stand in front of you. You can see it, you might be able to smell the cocoa and if you cut yourself a slice you'll be able to enjoy the delicious depth of flavour and texture. But if you keep your mind blank and don't allow yourself to have a thought about it (perhaps distracting yourself by imaging being stuck in a lift with the most boring person you know) what's your experience of it going to be? It's going to be extremely limited. It's a bit like mindlessly working your way through a tub of ice cream whilst watching TV. The only experience you'll have of it is an empty tub and more weight on your hips.

If this all seems a little difficult to accept, please don't take my word for it. You'll need to carry out your own experiments to explore this further. Notice what's going on throughout your day, pay attention to how you're feeling and start to recognise what thoughts are flitting through your mind at the time. Feeling calm and relaxed? What are you thinking? Feeling stressed? What do you notice in your mind? Has anything changed apart from your thoughts?

Pay attention to the situations where you feel peaceful and chilled one day and frazzled and stressed the next. Can you notice anything different about your thinking? Play at being a detective for a while and see if there are any patterns or trends you can spot.

Remember, what you uncover and notice for yourself is likely to have far more impact on your life and your stress levels than any arguments I could use to convince you. So play with these tasks, treat them lightly and have fun.

Linking thoughts and feelings may make perfect sense to you immediately or it might in some areas and not in others. It can be a doddle to see the connection between our thoughts and feelings of stress when we're sat waiting for the dentist or getting cross with a colleague who yet again has been rude and inconsiderate. In those circumstances, finding the connection between feelings of stress and thoughts may be obvious.

But surely there are lots of experiences in life where this couldn't possibly apply? If you're experiencing money problems or struggling with your health or at your wits end about arguments in a close relationship, how could your feelings be due to anything at all other than this particular, difficult, intransigent problem?

Of course, I'm not going to deny that bad things happen in life and when they do it's appropriate to feel grief, fear, rage or whatever strong emotion is there in the moment. This certainly isn't about any judgment about what we should think and how we ought to feel. All I'm hoping you get to see here is that there's a direct connection between our thoughts and our feelings and never our feelings and the outside world despite how real and obvious this might seem.

We live our lives in stress so often because of thoughts and emotions that have nothing to do with right here, right now but are rooted in thoughts about the past or the future. They're allowed free rein to run wild with potential, apocalyptic scenarios and then we wonder why we feel stressed!

I want you to understand that our feelings are not necessarily an accurate reflection of any situation we find ourselves in. Stressful feelings do not come from inherently stressful situations. Relaxed, chilled feelings do not come from innately calm circumstances. Granted, most of us have been living in this illusion for the majority of our lives but this doesn't make it any more truthful or real.

So if we can't trust our feelings to tell us anything worthwhile about what's happening to us, can we rely on them at all? What do they tell us? As far as letting us know about the quality of our thinking at any point, we can't rely on a better barometer. Our feelings are perfect in-the-moment mirrors of the thoughts passing through our mind. This doesn't mean that we need to try and change our thoughts to help us feel differently. It simply means *that* we think and we feel our thoughts in the moment and this is how we live in life.

I'll talk much more in the following chapters about how this has an impact on our stress but for the time being, spend some time noticing your thoughts about what's been covered here. Does it make complete sense or are there areas of life where you can't see how this could be true? Give yourself a little time to complete the "over to you" questions and then join me in the next chapter where we'll take a closer look at these thoughts of ours.

**Over to you**

Where have you been able to see the link between your thoughts and your feelings?

In which areas of your life do you find it more difficult to see this connection?

Where would you like to be able to see it more clearly?

# Chapter 8: Fearsome Heffalumps

**In which we investigate the role of thoughts in our feelings of stress and why we don't need to take our thinking seriously.**

Did you ever read Winnie-the-Pooh when you were a child? If you did you may recall how Piglet frightened himself by imagining a fierce Heffalump only to discover the creature didn't exist – it was Pooh with a jar of honey stuck on his head. And as we will discover in this chapter, our thoughts are at times our very own Heffalumps.

We all talk to ourselves constantly. There's a never-ending running commentary chatter that starts from the moment we wake up to the minute consciousness leaves us for sleep.

Sometimes, the voice in our head can seem sane and rational.

"It's time to leave for work."

"Don't forget to buy more milk and bread."

"Shall I go to that drink's party?"

We could almost be lulled into believing it's a benign, helpful presence with our dearest interests at heart.

But then there are other times when this voice is shrill and its harping tone is far from sympathetic.

"Did you really say that!!!! What sort of person says that sort of thing, don't you ever think before speaking? How could you have been such an idiot!"

"You're never going to achieve that – someone from your background, your age – who's going to take you seriously? Are you kidding me? You're far too old for that!"

Over decades of reading self-help books, I've been on a very long journey in my relationship with my thoughts as I've been encouraged to treat them in many different ways.

In my early twenties, despite a school life where had there been an award for "Shyest Girl in the Year", it would have been mine I was recruited as a trainer to run courses for an insurance company. No one was more surprised by this appointment than me. At this stage in my self-development journey, I was particularly influenced by the book, "Feel the Fear and Do It Anyway". So I threw myself into my work and despite constant fearful thoughts that even made me physically sick, I carried on and eventually came to love the thrill of standing in front of an audience, running courses.

Later, as my reading progressed, I was influenced by books that suggested my thoughts contained nuggets of valuable information that required exploration and analysis. So when thoughts like,

"You're not good enough, you can't handle this. You're no good at dealing with stress" floated into my mind, I convinced myself they must be there for a good reason. Some deep, wise part of me knew I needed to hear these messages before I did anything foolish and made a mess of my life.

I paid careful attention to those thoughts. Each one was thoroughly, painstakingly dissected to uncover which difficult, barely conscious memory they were associated with and then healed using some pretty natty mind techniques I picked up along the way. Eventually (or so the theory went) if I kept doing this long enough, I would uncover abundance and an easy path towards my dreams.

Later on in my journey, I learned to reframe thoughts, to metaphorically throw them up into the air, juggle each one to have a look at it from a different angle, turn them inside out and search for counter-arguments. Each thought had my full attention, reinforcing the idea that they were important, their message of value and I'd better take note of even those that flitted momentarily through my mind.

By the time I was in my late forties, this attention and analysis had got out of control and my metaphorical thought-knickers were well and truly in a twist. Although from the outside, I probably looked as if all was well, I was starting to suffer from stress, anxiety and a touch of depression from all this exhausting thought awareness.

But here's what I ultimately discovered.

Despite believing otherwise for so long, I've never been able to control what thoughts are going to arrive next in my mind and trying to do so, is a pointless exercise.

As an experiment, I've sat staring out of the window for a few moments to wait and see which thoughts turn up:

- ·A sudden memory of a little red, painted box my father brought me back from Norway decades ago (haven't thought of that in years) – no idea where that thought came from.
- ·Thoughts of the film I watched last night.
- ·A half-remembered conversation from the previous summer with a dear friend.

Until each of these thoughts popped up, there is no way I could have predicted any of them. And if you repeat this experiment, I guarantee you'll come to the same conclusion.

So you may be wondering if we can't control what we're thinking, how does that help us deal with stressed thoughts and what difference is knowing this going to make to our anxiety? Well here's what I didn't know for such a long time - whilst none of the thoughts coming into our mind are under our control nor do we have to pay attention to them once they arrive either. We don't have to accept them as "The Truth" and we certainly never have to view them as a reflection of who we are.

These thoughts are not necessarily telling us anything useful – you can think of them as impersonal, ghost-like entities (or scary Heffalump monsters) that float around in the air and every so often happen to attach themselves to our mind. As I have discovered, this one idea can be transformational - it means we are not our thoughts.

I used to be so good at believing what my unpleasant thoughts said about me or trusting they were able to predict my future abilities or lack of them. But as you start to give yourself a little mental distance from your thoughts, watch them objectively as an impartial observer might, your detachment from them grows. And then it's easier to see which thoughts might be worth staying with for a while and ignoring those that aren't.

This is where you have a choice.

I don't mean here that having thoughts, any type of thought, is something we need to avoid. We're not trying to create some inner-zen, quiet mind zone with which we float thoughtlessly through life. Rather, taking our thoughts, all of them with a pinch of salt, treating each of them lightly is the best way to inhibit any tendencies they may have to take themselves too seriously and turn into "thought divas".

And then a funny thing starts to happen.

As you pay less attention to the insistent, loud thoughts in your mind, as you begin to ignore the critical and the damming, they get quieter and vanish all by themselves. Without your constant care and attention, they simply wither away (very much like house plants under my care). Until eventually, thinking becomes less cluttered, leaving room for the clear, spacious mind we so often crave when we're stressed.

If I had to point to any aspect of this book that has had the most impact on me personally, it would be what I have covered in this chapter. It seems simple enough, the idea that we don't have to believe our thoughts; that there really is no need to take them seriously. Doing this gives us so much inner freedom and over time I have noticed a lightness to life that has become more and more apparent.

Of course, this begs the question, how do you *know* the difference between a helpful thought and one which can be discarded? Well, all I can say about this is that there seems to be a different quality between the two which over time, you'll become wise to. For me, the more useful thoughts seem to have a sturdier quality to them whereas not so helpful ones seem more frantic but you will learn to distinguish between them yourself. But in the next chapter, I will say more about the characteristics of unhelpful, stress-inducing thoughts to get you started.

**Over to you**

When have you been able to ignore your thoughts and carry on regardless?

Where in your life could you start paying less attention to negative or worrisome thoughts?

# Chapter 9: Dancing with the Little Red Riding Hood Wolf

**In which we discover the different ways our thinking can stress and frighten us.**

As you will find for yourself, when we start to take our thoughts less seriously, it becomes clear that much of what goes on in our head can be ignored and treated like some irritating, drunk person who is making as much sense as my friend's pet goldfish, Cyril.

In this chapter, I wanted to highlight some of the ways our thoughts can trip us up and cause problems by scaring us and making us anxious (eek! Is that a scary wolf hiding over there?) not because we need to do anything about them, but because becoming aware of their favourite disguises can help us spot them for what they are. When we shine a spotlight on these villains it's far, far easier to take them less seriously.

## Overthinking

I often think of the mind as being like a fairground. When it's stressed and our thoughts are flying around, we're taken spinning on a giant, frantic rollercoaster. There's no space for silence, reflection or contemplation as thoughts dip and dive, weave backwards and forwards, jolting us up to the heavens and back down earthwards at a frantic, whirling pace.

Being strapped into this heart-stopping ride is how we feel when we're trying to focus and analyse when under pressure and stressed – a hundred thoughts and questions rushing around in our head, but no space or ability to think clearly. We may find it exciting living at this mental speed or we may wish for something more peaceful. But ultimately this intensity can't be maintained indefinitely and sooner or later we're going to come crashing to a standstill.

Contrast this with the sedate elegance of the old fashioned carousel. Elegant, coloured horses carry their rider on a slow, gentle gallop around and around, up and down. There's plenty of time to admire the view, take in the experience, look ahead, turn our head and notice what's behind us. This is like the mind when thought is slower and calmer. We're able to take in so much more of life and there's far more capacity to recognise what's important.

A slower, calmer more peaceful state of mind is what many of us are hoping to find and why we enjoy activities that capture our attention and require our focus like climbing or dancing or even more sedentary activities like painting or knitting. We instinctively know how pleasurable it feels for the mind to slow down to this pace and that's why we turn to techniques such as meditation or deep breathing to deliberately encourage it even though they're not necessary to achieve this state.

Unfortunately, when we're feeling stressed, I can guarantee we're caught up in the overthinking mind rather than the chilled-out version as I discovered from my own experience. Whenever I was going through money worries, it was those fast, incessant thoughts that created so much stress.

"How are we going to cope?"
  "What if my husband doesn't ever get another job?"
  "What if he gets ill?"
  "What sort of work could I do that would pay enough?"
  "Can we pay the electricity bill?"
  "What other bills might be coming soon?"

And on and on and on.

So what was going on inside my head?

In this state, my thinking would flit very quickly from one concern to the next. I was overthinking and analysing problems and issues that hadn't occurred and might never come our way. I was making up information and problems and trying to make decisions and choices that didn't need to be made at that time when there was still as yet, no choice to be made.

It was like stressing about going out for a meal, making up a menu ahead of time and trying to decide whether I would fancy the fish or the chicken. "I expect this is what they're going to offer but what if the meat dishes are too spicy?" All made up (although the illusion of reality is there, I will admit), all created in my mind until we actually visit the restaurant and discover they only serve pizza.

Is it any wonder we get stressed?

Whilst our stress may come from these premature decisions, in reality, much of it comes from busy, fast thoughts, from overthinking and it's impossible to think clearly when our mind is on overdrive.

## Diva thinking

Another way our thoughts can slide into a trap is by falling into what I call diva thinking. You know the sort – making mountains out of the smallest problems, demanding our attention and throwing thought-tantrums by over-playing the importance and significance of problems that are *sure* to last forever. We anticipate doom, gloom and total destruction at every corner.

"I'm going to make this the worst mess ever."
   "Everything always goes wrong for me."

In his book, Learned Optimism, Martin Seligman talks about a couple of types of thinking which he calls permanence and pervasiveness that are the foundation of this kind of diva thinking.

## Permanence

Our thinking predicts the bad times are going to persist; the events and situations that cause us problems are going to stay with us indefinitely. "Always" and "never" are keywords. So when we are stuck in this sort of diva thinking we will have thoughts like;
   "I'm *always* going to struggle with this."
   "Things *never* work out for me."
   "I'll *never* have any money."

## Pervasiveness

In this type of thinking, we apply our conclusions from specific circum-stances, turn them into generalisations and make huge assumptions about vast swathes of our life. For example, having difficulties learning how to turn out the perfect soufflé turns into a full-scale rant about how utterly useless we are at everything.

Or struggling to make conversation with one group of people, on one specific afternoon becomes "Why am I so bad at making new friends?" completely discounting a lovely chat the previous week with a new neighbour who has just moved into the street. Of course, these generalisations are never going to be completely accurate. Even someone who feels they fail at so much in their life will have been a success somewhere. For even the most accident-prone person there will have been luck at some time down the line.

**Increasing our awareness of overthinking and diva thoughts**

Both overthinking and diva thoughts can be addictive - our minds love the drama and excitement of chaos, speed and life's ups and downs. But as with all stimulants as we become more aware of the impact they have, the more sensitive to them we become and ultimately, the more intolerant.

Now when I hear any of these types of thought in my head, over time I've developed an inner warning system, a wry internal chuckle, an "Oops! There I go again." thought that has become increasingly aware of overthinking and diva thoughts.

In no way is this internal mechanism perfect. Of course, like everyone else, there are times when my thoughts come from a mood so low that they come in fast and furiously and I remain oblivious to their true nature as "just thoughts". I can find that I'm swamped by them. But on the whole, the warning system works.

This doesn't mean to say that we need to "do" anything. Again, I am not going to suggest a specific technique to alter these types of thoughts and you won't need to try and change them – simplicity is the key here. As you will see more and more throughout this book, the very act of "noticing" is all that's required. To be aware of them is all that you need to "do".

It's a bit like becoming incredibly angry and frustrated when we have to pay huge sums of money in rent and worry how we're going to afford it, only to suddenly recall that we are playing a game of monopoly. We are dealing with pretend money and a few rolls of the dice and someone is probably going to land on our rather plush hotel in Park Lane. We don't have to do anything to go from lost in the game to remembering – that awareness is enough to change our perspective and it's exactly the same process with our thoughts.

**Over to you**

In which situations is your overthinking triggered?

When do you tend to be susceptible to diva thinking?

# Chapter 10: It's Not All Spoonfuls of Sugar

**In which we learn why positive thinking is not as important as we may think it is.**

What I have written about so far in this book is not about positive thinking our way through life. After all, there can be nothing more irritating than being with someone whose relentless cheerful whistles continually assault your ears or doesn't stop laughing in the face of persistent disaster (or is that just my intolerance?). I am not trying to turn you into a permanently, happy fairy (heaven forbid) or talk you into turning rainy days into hours of sunshine.

This isn't what this is about.

It's not about having to change a negative thought about stress into something more acceptable. It's never allowing only lovely, fluffy happy thoughts (even if that were ever possible) reframing negative ones, or gritting of teeth to force ourselves to see the positive in every awful, grim situation.

It's not about hard work, or having to "do".

It's a way of being, of allowing it all and not being afraid to experience every single emotion fully. No exceptions.

I was brought up near the sea. I've always loved swimming in the summer and picnicking on the beach, But for me, beaches have a special charm in the winter – in the fog and rain and wind, when there's no one else around. It's all part of my beach experience whatever the season. It would be very easy to place judgment on which is better – summer or winter. But they both have their beauty, one is not better than the other.

And the same is true of our feelings. All emotions have their place and whilst we may prefer excitement over fear, joy over anger we can embrace it all.

As Sydney Banks said;
   "If the only thing that people learned was not to be afraid of their experience that alone would change the world."

Feelings are nothing to fear, even those pesky feelings of stress that threaten to overwhelm us at times. The miracle is that we feel any of it, that we have the consciousness to recognise what we feel, to experience a whole range of glorious, human emotions. When an event we long for is canceled, we don't win the prize or get the job, it's completely appropriate and normal to feel mad, bad, angry, frustrated, or miserable.

Even in the midst of suffering we also know the pain will pass and eventually the feelings will move on. Once we let go of the preference for this or that experience – preferring joy over boredom, excitement over frustration, each emotion simply becomes another part of the rich experience of life.

None of it stays with us forever.

Its pointless wasting time and energy trying to monitor for good (acceptable) and bad (unacceptable) feelings, attempting mental acrobatics to try to transform the ones we're not happy with when we could live, experience and allow emotions to move through. And that includes feelings of stress.

**Over to you**

Which emotions do you label as negative or ones to avoid in your own life?

What tactics do you use to try and push or move them away?

How could you do less to change your emotions and more to allow them to move through you?

# Part 3: Somewhere Over The Rainbow

"Stand and deliver!"

These words would have struck terror into the heart of travellers in the 18th century. But anyone passing near the village I live in on their way from London to Bath to "take the waters" faced an additional risk. At the time the area was famous for its gang of naked highwaymen who regularly terrorised affluent travellers – presumably their thoughts were that victims would be preoccupied with something other than their faces making later recognition tricky. For a while, they were successful and evaded capture. But inevitably their luck eventually ran out and they were tried and executed (fully clothed I suspect) in a nearby market town.

Although I can guarantee there's no nakedness or highway robbery in this part of the book we're also going to be looking in a different direction to the one you might expect, to deal with your stress. And you may be surprised to learn, this doesn't involve a list of techniques to help you achieve inner calm whilst havoc is being created all around you.

It's far simpler than that. It's about looking in the direction of the cause of our stress rather than treating symptoms and once we have done this we realise there is so much less to do than we might initially think.

# Chapter 11: No Kissing of Frogs Required

**In which we establish how little we really need to do to manage our feelings of stress.**

Now we've got to the part of the book where I'll explain what you can do about stress. And unlike the princess in the fairy tale, you're not even going to have to kiss any frogs – I bet you're relieved about that!

As I've said all along (you might have thought I have laboured this excessively, but it's such an important point), this isn't a book about techniques and anti-stress busting methods. I know this seems utterly bizarre given we're so used to thinking we have to work hard to make progress, to "do" and that change requires effort and attention.

Think about all those problems you're having with midlife, concerns about your health, the difficult boss, the unpromising relationship, niggling money worries. Do you remember I explained how our feelings of stress and overwhelm (and happiness for that matter) never come from these external causes even though it seems as if they have *everything* to do with our stress?

They are simply a consequence of our thinking, no matter how tricky this can be to accept and how difficult it is to see at times. The beauty of this understanding though is once seen, everything changes miraculously.

The other morning I was awake at 2.00 am feeling miserable pondering the 'State of My Life' and getting lost as I slid down into a deep, dark hole reviewing all that didn't appear to be working - finances, fitness, looks, friends, job prospects, dealing with a teenage daughter, writing ability and lack of any worthwhile accomplishments or achievements in my life. It was a *very* comprehensive list and cheery thoughts were suspiciously absent!

But the moment I mentally stepped away from my thoughts and remembered how the same circumstances seemed very different when I was naturally more upbeat and optimistic during the day, everything transformed. I saw positive aspects of my life that I literally couldn't see when I was feeling down. This happened by seeing anew an insight that had come to me before, noticing afresh the relationship between my feelings and my thoughts from this new perspective – not having to do this or that technique.

When we know where our stress is coming from, when we recognise that it's arising from our thoughts, never the outside environment this has a number of implications.

Firstly, the symptoms of stress seem to take care of themselves. We no longer need to concern ourselves with not being able to sleep, racing thoughts, feelings of overwhelm, or whatever our version of stress looks and feels like. They come from mistaken thinking and when we remember this at some point they disappear without us having to meditate, go on a spa day or book a series of therapy sessions to uncover the cause in our past. The best way to treat them is to just do nothing and let them take care of themselves.

Yes, you read that correctly! Do absolutely nothing! And you may be wondering how this can possibly be true.

Our feelings never remain static. Even deep, turbulent feelings like rage or grief, have their time and, if we let them, will move through us. It's impossible to feel one emotion forever no matter how stormy and out of control, it feels at the time, no matter how entrenched. Even the deepest despair, the most consuming anger, sooner or later passes and we're onto feeling something else.

Look at small children, petulant and angry one moment, full of wonder and joy the next. Their moods ebb and flow, rise and fall, from one to the next. And so can ours if we allow them to. Sometimes it can feel as if our emotions become stuck when we resist them, push them down and try to pretend they don't exist. Then we wonder why we feel emotionally frozen!

When we allow ourselves to feel our stressful emotions, not to be afraid of them and simply let them flow through us, we make life so much easier if we remember that, given time, there is nothing for us to do – no self-medication required, no stress management techniques necessary. Those feelings will move through us because, as we're already seen, thoughts flow in and out. And in fact, meddling with them, trying to do something with them can often mean they stick around for longer. Our emotions come from our thoughts - thoughts can't get stuck and so emotions don't need to either.

I hope you're starting to get an inkling of how far this understanding can take you once you fully grasp that emotions only ever come from inside your own head. When your thoughts change, your feelings follow and you can give up using so much energy trying to manipulate circumstances in the external world to help you feel better.

You can also stop struggling to manage your feelings of stress. Once we get that stress is only ever an inside job, learning more stress management techniques seems pointless and irrelevant. The need to change the external world because we're stressed simply dissolves. There's nothing to do to change that experience and we can just let the feelings move on in their own time.

That said, it doesn't mean we don't have situations in our life that in our calm, peaceful moments we know we need to do something about. Maybe it *is* time to leave the difficult workplace, tackle our financial problems or take charge of our health. But the distinction here is important. If you have taken on board what I've said to this point, sorting out these issues and problems arises not from a feeling of stress but from a calm, deep, clear, inner knowing. We are so much more able to come up with helpful ideas and take the next steps from this place rather than from a feeling of frazzled, urgency and "I can't take this a moment longer!"

So in the next chapter, we'll look at how that works from this understanding and how you can begin to tap into a source of guidance and inspiration that's already there within you.

**Over to you**

Where have you been able to step back from your own thinking?

When are you starting to see the real cause of your stress?

# Chapter 12: We're our Own Knightess in Shining Armour

**In which we uncover how to change those situations that need to be tackled, without stress.**

Ancient Egyptians believed the key to a comfortable afterlife was to be buried with a selection of goods to take with them but today, few people request to have toasters and kettles crammed into coffins beside them. And although we like to think of ourselves as more sophisticated than these ancient peoples, we're really no closer to knowing what's "beyond". It's simply that our ideas surrounding life and death have shifted. So let's hope we're not kicking ourselves when we discover that household appliances would in fact be useful in the afterlife!

Having said that, in other areas, what's seen as natural next steps and solutions have changed as our understanding has shifted and deepened. In medieval times, suggestions for fertility included inserting the brains of a male and female bird into the woman before trying to conceive or smearing dove fat and brains onto "privy parts" for a couple of days. You'll be pleased to hear the medical profession no longer recommends these practices - as our knowledge about the causes of infertility has increased, remedies and solutions have naturally evolved.

Similarly for us, as our understanding deepens of how life works our expectation of what we need to feel safe in the world, to thrive and make progress, changes. And this all happens with no effort, no work. No self-development techniques are required, there's no need to explore our past or uncover negative beliefs - just simple, effortless transformation that happens as a result of an ever-deepening comprehension.

It's as if our understanding has taken a ride in a hot air balloon and as we rise upwards into a clear, blue sky we get to see the world, or as in this case, life, in a different way. We see further. We have a wider, clearer perspective. We notice things we never could have glimpsed from the ground. And our understanding of the geography of the land is transformed instantly. Once seen, it's never completely forgotten and there's no way of undoing this appreciation of how life works.

It's ours forever.

Think of this book as your own hot air balloon, a way of taking a fresh look at how you see stress. Let's say, for argument's sake, that you're starting to look at the stress response in a far more positive light. You've got a clearer understanding of where it's coming from in your own life and you're settling into the idea that you're not in need of a psychological band-aid. You're not broken and you don't need fixing. From now on, we can all sit back and relax and watch the world float by.

The problem is that life is still going to throw trials, tragedies and problems at us whether we feel stressed or not. Life isn't going to back off simply because we're looking at it in a different, more relaxed way. I'm not suggesting that all we need to do is withdraw from the world and allow life to simply happen to us. Our lives are there for us to become fully involved in and immersed with. Even though we know now where difficult feelings are coming from – inside our head and not the outside world - there are still going to be times when we need to make decisions and take steps forward.

Despite knowing my boss isn't the cause of my stress, I might choose to learn a different way to respond to her or find another job. Whilst recognising my anxious thinking around my health isn't what's making me feel bad, I might still want to find ways to improve how I look after myself. There are always going to be changes to be made, problems to be tackled. But the difference is that now we are in the mental and emotional space where we can start to deal more effectively with the problem that previously would have caused us so much stress.

But what steps can we take if we're stuck in uncertainty and unsure what to do?

Do you ever wrestle with a stressful problem and can't sleep at night because your mind uses that time to very kindly and helpfully present you with a Hammer House horror of likely scenarios? Your thinking is all over the place, flits from one worry to the next and the solution seems obscured by a jumble of worry and doubt. Then the next day, when you've finally managed to get a little sleep, you're out on a quiet walk and the solution jumps, fully formed into your mind.

If you think back over your life – when have you ever had your best ideas? Has it been A) when you're knuckling down hard, analysing a situation to death, determined you're going to come up with a good idea, whatever it takes. Or has it been B) when you've mentally given up and have gone off to do something else? Maybe allowing yourself a spot of time with your favourite hobby, out for a walk, or enjoying a warm shower.

Then boom all of a sudden, completely out of nowhere, the perfect solution comes hurtling fully formed into your mind. And the crazy thing is it will seem so perfect and simple that you'll wonder why on earth you didn't think of it earlier.

In the past, I used to obsess over finding the answer or solution to problems, grappling with the conundrum until it felt as if my head was going to explode with the strain. I believed that problem solving involved a certain amount of mental struggle and intensity and if it didn't feel like this, I wasn't trying hard enough.

But it doesn't have to be this way.

Once we allow our thoughts to float in and out of our awareness without taking too much notice of them we have the mental space to come up with new ideas for dealing with whatever needs to be dealt with. Sometimes it might simply be a quiet idea to phone someone or take a small action, a nudge in a new direction.

These flashes of inspiration, sudden "ah-ha" moments are what I call insights. They arrive completely out of the blue, often feel novel and fresh and they are perfectly suited to the demands and needs of our specific problem or issue.

I know a couple more things about insights.

First of all, I can guarantee they *will* show up, that you have the capacity to have them. If you're worrying you might be the exception to the rule because you're in no way creative and the last great idea you had was four years ago and even that was a bit suspect, I want to put your mind at rest. You do have this ability – everyone does. If you're not convinced, it might be worth spending a little time, remembering all those times, when you suddenly knew what to do about a problem, or you had an inner knowing about a step you needed to take.

Don't get caught up in any worries that you're not creative because I promise it's built into the system of how your mind works. In fact, it's so ordinary and every-day that we often don't even recognise it for what it is.

What I can't guarantee, and nor can we force, is asking for these insights on demand. They're elusive and slippery and they'll show up when they show up. Now I know that's frustrating – fancy not being able to rely on a great idea exactly when you want it! Except I have found that mentally giving up on expecting one, even for a while, is when they're more likely to show up.

When our thinking seems stuck and we're frustrated, trying to analyse and twist our mind into knots with thoughts going round and round in circles in our head, there's no space for something new to emerge. And although insight is available to us even when we're under pressure, what really helps is a relaxed feeling and a spacious mind with our attention on nothing much particularly.

My best advice when you feel in need of inspiration is to give yourself a break. Go off and do something you enjoy, that makes you feel good, that gives you the opportunity to completely forget what it is you're trying so hard to get insight around. Stay open to the possibility the answer could be something new, something completely unexpected. And don't forget these insights can work for the grand, complicated issues of our life as well as the small, seemingly insignificant, humdrum ones of daily life too.

As part of an online training programme I was on recently, I needed to attend a live training session that started on a public holiday. The only problem is that our Wi-Fi connection is particularly poor during weekends and holidays. It's rarely a problem but I really wanted to attend the training and didn't want to miss any of the sessions.

I played around with solutions for days. Various options and ideas sprang to mind. I could ask a friend with a more reliable connection if I could borrow a room for a few hours or go and sit in a coffee shop. Both were reasonable ideas. But then suddenly it occurred to me out of the blue, after I'd been mulling this over for days, that I could stay an extra day with my mother who I'd been planning to visit with my daughter and complete the training at her house. She lives in a rural area in the country where everyone is always out doing wholesome outdoor activities and there's plenty of Wi-Fi capacity.

It was the perfect solution and once it had entered my head, seemed the easiest, most obvious thing to do. I was amazed it hadn't occurred to me before! In fact, this is what I love about insights because, in hindsight, they so often have an "obvious" quality to them.

So be prepared to mentally give up, knock the struggle on the head and go and do something else and start noticing what happens. It doesn't need to be complicated. I've found so often, with a wry smile, that it's surprising how easy and straightforward the solution turns out to be. If it all seems to be getting too complicated, that's a sure sign to wait for something simpler to turn up and don't forget to trust that it'll show up when it shows up.

**Over to you**

When have you had a sudden flash of insight that's been just what you needed?

Which area would you like insight around now?

# Chapter 13: Should Rapunzel Let Down Her Long Hair or Settle in With a Good Book?

**In which we look at how to stop fretting about making decisions and how to make them more easily.**

Stay in a marriage or search for a new partner? Make the most of a secure but staid career or create an exciting new business? Splash out on the sparkly shoes or make do with the plain?

Our lives revolve around a constant stream of decisions, some with implications that will last for decades, others are no more life-changing than choosing between a biscuit or a large slice of cake ( I'm always in favour of the latter). And whilst there's nothing to stop us from resorting to the ever-faithful "flip a coin" technique, consult tea leaves or ask a friend, insight can very definitely shine a beacon of light through the dark night of indecision.

For many decisions, the time to make them is as soon as they appear as questions in our heads. Sitting in a restaurant with a menu full of delicious choices there's no point mulling it over for the next few hours. But with others we suffer from premature 'decisionitis', we're too impatient to wait, we dislike sitting in the uncomfortable position of uncertainty. We want to skip ahead and get ourselves caught in loops of doubt, forcing choices before they are decisions to be made.

My daughter sometimes gets herself into a complete state by trying to decide her future career, now. Should she look after horses or become a teacher? Would she be happiest being a marine biologist or a novelist?

As I write this, she's twelve.

You and I both know how much can change by the time she needs to make that choice. Her ultimate career may turn out to be one that's not yet invented. If she insists on making the decision now, her choice may have become completely redundant by the times she's working (there's very little demand for lighthouse keepers or for anyone to light street lamps at night these days). Over the next few years, her interests are inevitably going to change, circumstances will evolve and this decision can remain fluid right up until the point when it's time to be made.

Trying to rush decisions, making them ahead of time, is as pointless as trying to choreograph an entire discussion with a friend three weeks in advance. Not only do we have absolutely no idea which topics of conversation will seem relevant at the time, even if we know our friend well, how could we ever predict how they're going to respond or what they're going to say? Far more sensible to turn up and respond to what happens in the moment.

If there's an optimal time for making a decision, there's also a state of mind that helps and big hint, it isn't when we're caught up in turmoil and worry. When you feel up to your eyes in stress, are lost in the depths of a low mood, or have a strong sense of urgency that this problem desperately needs to be sorted now, once and for all, trying to force a decision is not going to work. Making important decisions is not recommended when you're in the midst of a stress thought storm. It's much more helpful to wait until it's past. Sitting it out until our feelings are more stable which shows our thinking is more helpful and clearer, is a wiser idea.

Once we start to tap into this deep inner knowing or internal wisdom, it becomes obvious that we *do* know what needs to be done. Doors need to be slammed shut on doomed love matches, gooey chocolate cakes need to be left on supermarket shelves and tickets for exciting new adventures need to be booked.

But if we've fallen into the middle of a stress response, when our thinking is dodgy and our mood is low we're not in the best frame of mind to make decisions. Our thinking is contaminated with the dust and dirt of pessimism - we lack the clarity to see clearly. That would be like deciding to always wear wellies and thick coats because we once looked out of the window and the weather was dreary and grey. Contrast this with when our thinking and mood are on a more even keel and then we are able to think more clearly, make more helpful decisions. We have a more realistic grasp of the reality of any situation.

Choose your timing wisely.

I learned this the hard way in my relationships. When I look back at my twenties, I can't help concluding I was a pain in the arse girlfriend. Not because I was overly possessive. jealous or high maintenance but because I believed if the relationship seemed to be going even the slightest way off track, it was probably best to dissect and analyse it in teeny, tiny detail. *And* it was best to get into an argument about it when I was feeling most insecure or fraught.

This strategy never ended well (I'm sure even the least talented relationship agony aunt could have told me that!). I remember with some embarrassment those circular discussions that from no one's perspective could ever have been seen as a fun, productive way to spend a wet, dreary Sunday afternoon.

Of course, later when I came across this understanding, it became clear that talking about relationship issues was never useful or helpful when either party was feeling low, grumpy, or ready for an argument. Rather, the conversations went so much better if issues in the relationship were discussed when both of us were feeling light, buoyant and optimistic.

Funnily enough, my relationships seemed far more successful after this.

**My tips for making decisions**

- By all means, do your research. Find out about your options, explore all possibilities and use insight to provide you with fresh and juicy ideas. When it's time for a decision to be made, you'll feel it. You will have a feeling of simply "knowing" what to do. Waiting until that time is going to save you much internal angst.


- If you are pondering several alternatives and one option really does make no more sense over the other, then play with the possibility that your final choice may in fact be irrelevant. Both options will bring advantages and lessons and sometimes, the important thing is to just get on and make a decision.

- The best decisions are usually made when you're in an easy, quiet state of mind and if you're feeling a sense of panic or urgency, it's best to leave the life-changing choices for another time.

- Decisions tend to have built-in parameters for the best time to be made and when that time has been reached, very often either the right choice becomes very obvious or there are additional factors to be considered that could never have been anticipated or predicted.

## Looking for the whispers

As I've settled into living life this way, I have noticed how insights arrive with more regularity and I've become more skilled at noticing solutions that haven't come from within me but from something in the outside world I'd previously been blind to. I've probably been walking past the answer day in day out not seeing until some perceptual filter is lifted and there it is right in front of me. It's been there all along but it takes the space from an internal shift for me to see it. It's what an early mentor of mine, Gill Edwards called "listening to the whispers".

For years my young daughter wanted a pony but our response was always a firm but hopefully very loving, "no". Not only was it a time and financial expense we didn't want to saddle ourselves with (pun alert), we also knew little about keeping a pony healthy.

But my daughter kept saving her pocket money and, to keep up morale, we had regular chats about keeping her dream alive. I reminded her if she was really keen even if we didn't know "how" this would work, to keep on trusting that it could be a reality one day. I was trying to tread a very fine balance between not getting her hopes up and not letting her fall into a heap of despondency.

And then when she was about ten and away on a residential school trip, a Facebook post popped up from the riding stables where she had lessons about the possibility of sharing a pony. Access to a pony on three days a week, responsibility for caring for and riding the pony on those days and a fixed monthly price with no extra charges. Most importantly, all the tricky looking-after -a-pony decisions were made by the riding stables.

I suspect I'd seen these posts many times before, but on this particular day, a light bulb lit up in my head and I knew we could make it work. I was in touch with the stables within minutes, expressing our interest. There were many details to sort out – but – they had exactly the pony I knew my daughter was after, (and this was no mean feat as he was extremely popular) and on the days we could make to fit in with other activities.

We looked after him for a year and a half until my daughter got too big for him and then we moved onto another pony share at the stables. My daughter grew in confidence and there was never a complaint from her about any of the chores. She loved every minute of it and it was and still is an amazing experience for her. What worked for us in this situation was keeping the dream alive and staying relaxed and open-minded so that we could see solutions and answers when they showed up.

When you're in a situation you need to change, keep your senses and mind open for new or unusual solutions to come from other people, your day to day world, or things you hear or see and be ready to be amazed by how easy and straightforward the solution will seem.

**Over to you**

When have you struggled with decision making and what happened?

When did a decision seem to make itself and how did that work out?

Where do you need to start looking for your own whispers?

# Chapter 14: Falling Back into a Sleeping Beauty Snooze

**In which we find out how falling back into believing our level of stress comes from "out there" is part of the journey and completely normal.**

Have you ever experienced times when you float through life from one happy coincidence to the next? Problems are solved with ease and you do what needs to be done without drama or fuss - even the humdrum and the routine seem miraculous and joyous.

And then wham! Cracks appear. Something drags you down and you're stumbling back into confusion and feeling stuck. Life gets messy and bad-tempered. Your focus narrows and contracts and you wonder if you'll ever drift through anything again. You're caught up in frantic thinking and a busy mind and before you know it, you're stressing about some circumstance or problem that's showing up in your life. What's worse, insignificant problems that you tackle with so little effort when you're feeling more resourceful, have developed into "impossible to climb" mountains.

You've fallen back into believing your state of mind comes from a situation out there – from your age, relationships, money, too much work, not enough work. You find yourself yearning for something new, something else in your life, to make you feel differently, something to solve all these problems that are showing up. You sigh with regret because you haven't got the perfect job, income, partner, or home and become obsessed with how great you'd feel if you had these things.

We can all get caught up. And at times like these, we forget there's a rhythm even to the ups and downs of life. We're human and part of that human experience is to get tied up in believing once again, that feelings come from out there.

Relax – it's all working out perfectly.

I've been exploring this understanding for a few years and still every now and then momentarily get wound up in stress and anxiety and completely forget what it is I'm responding to. I fall asleep once more, like Sleeping Beauty, to how our experience is created. Once more there are dogs to be cross with for shaking mud all over the ceiling, tempers continue to fray and the pressure of countless tasks to be done mounts up as I worry about this situation or that problem.

Despite my best intentions, from time to time I collapse back into the illusion that external factors can make me feel a certain way. I still have moments when I hear the volume of my voice rise, my tone sharpens, and I feel adrenaline coursing through my body because I believe my feelings are caused by my daughter's behaviour or a driver who cut me up so rudely in busy traffic. Sometimes this flares up suddenly out of nowhere, other times, it's the slow, drawn-out burn of days of forgetting where my experience is really coming from.

At one time these reactions would have sent me into a panic and a self-critical spiral. But I want to reassure you such relapses are perfectly normal, they're simply the way life works. What I can't promise is that you'll never get stressed, anxious, or feel overwhelmed again and you'll breeze through life oblivious to any difficulty or setback. This understanding isn't able to provide an "escape from stress forever" card.

But what I have noticed is that when I've fallen into a relapse, it seems to take less time and mental effort for me to shift back out to this awareness of what's really going on and how this thought- created reality works. When I am lost in stress, eventually, sooner or later something softens and I remember I am not my thoughts or responses.

Then all of a sudden, hey presto, I'll pop back out of struggle into recognition and a calmer space. The illusion dissolves once more and I realise there's nothing to fix or solve. It's simply about looking in a different direction once again, seeing what comes to mind, noticing the connection between thought and feeling and my role in creating what I'm experiencing. Whilst the situation causing me stress won't have changed, usually not even by one tiny jot, everything will have shifted.

My mind will become quieter, my feelings soothed.

You may be teetering on the edge of this understanding or you may find you're already relaxing into life more. However far you've come I can guarantee at some point, you'll get caught up in stress, anxiety, struggle or overwhelm once again. Don't emotionally beat yourself up or get disheartened. Don't agonise or compare yourself with how much faster you think others can make sense of all of this.

It's not a race or a competition. There are no prizes for getting this faster or deeper than anyone else.

I promise you if you keep exploring and experimenting in this direction there will come a day when you'll amaze yourself. You'll look back and notice your feelings and actions are so very different from your old responses and it will feel wonderful, exhilarating even.

Then and only then will you start to notice how far you've come.

**Over to you**

How could you relax more into this understanding?

Where have you already seen it working in your life?

Which situations seem to trigger forgetfulness for you?

# Part Four – Living Happily Ever After

This began as a book about stress but I hope you are getting an inkling of how tackling feelings of midlife stress and overwhelm is just the beginning of the change that is possible for us. Once we understand the connection between our feelings and thoughts, when we begin to see where our experience comes from, inevitably a host of other (often surprising) benefits start showing up.

In this part of the book, I'd like to share with you some unexpected consequences I saw with this understanding that have had a profound impact on my life. On reflection, it hasn't simply been about finding a way to cure my feelings of stress and overwhelm - it's gone far beyond that.

So even if it's not entirely clear how this works for you just yet, if there are glimmers or cracks of light shining through in your understanding, that's enough. That's all that's ever required to start making progress.

I promise you, as you continue your exploration of how thought creates our reality, you will see more. It may be a slow, gentle meander or a more energetic dash – you get to decide on the pace and intensity. But stay with it and you'll start to notice other parts of your life become easier, lighter and more joyful.

# Chapter 15: Mirror, Mirror on the Wall, Where is the Most Relaxed Place of Them All?

**In which we establish how normal and everyday peace of mind really is.**

I've written a satisfying chunk of this book whilst away for a few days beside the sea. Happy, lazy days spent with my daughter, swimming in the harbour, feasting on fish and chips eaten out of paper, walking along the shore and breathing invigorating, salty air.

It's been glorious.

As I've settled into these simple, reflective days, I've noticed how my mind has become quieter. Time has stretched languidly and I've lived happily in each moment. I've been for long walks and barely had a thought other than noticing the beauty of the landscape around me. And the mental space has created room for insights to pop up regularly about this writing and other parts of my life.

Of course, this is easy-peasy when you're away on holiday with the cares and concerns of life far away. How difficult *can* it be to feel relaxed and at peace when you're surrounded by beautiful views, enjoying lazy schedules and no irritating colleagues or customers to disturb the sense of calm? Although a still, quiet mind isn't a given even in tranquil settings it certainly feels as if it's less effort to tap into when we're in such places.

There was a time when I would have assumed the only way to settle my mind would have been to take myself away on a lovely holiday, such as this one, or commit to hours of meditation or deep breathing. In other words, I would have needed to create the circumstances or engage in some activity for it to occur.

Now I know a quiet, spacious mind requires none of this, it's our natural default. When we stop living frantically, rushing around, filling our mind with worries and stresses, the mental equivalent of junk food, it naturally settles all by itself. There is nothing we have to do to find this state, no skill we need to learn, master or develop. There's no need to travel to deserted spiritual hot spots, read books or adopt complicated, daily routines - it's more about letting go and seeing all thoughts as impersonal that we choose to follow or not.

Mentally doing less is the key to unlocking its treasures. It's about settling down into an experience that's already there inside every one of us. Once uncovered, it will seem more than a little familiar. Even as stressed midlife women, it's a feeling we'll recognise as it's already part of our experience even if we haven't understood its significance before.

The truth is, it's every-day and mundane.

So ordinary in fact we might not have been aware of its true value. This peace of mind was ours when we were children and it's a way of being that's still available to us – perhaps not as often as we would like, maybe we only catch glimpses. But acknowledging this state of mind and exploring this understanding will encourage it to be a more regular companion. Somehow knowing it's there and understanding how thought really works seems to encourage it to be with us more frequently.

These days increasingly, it's a part of my daily life. It can be noticing birds hopping around the garden when I take a moment to drink a cup of tea. Or watching my husband laugh with a friend or enjoying the sensation of a swim. It doesn't seem to require a deliberate act of bringing my attention to the present moment rather it seems to be simply a by-product of this understanding and having a quieter mind. It's like enjoying the benefits of meditation without having to drum up the discipline to set time aside each day to sit quietly with my eyes closed and chase away unwanted thoughts.

As far as I'm concerned, that's a huge bonus.

But is it possible to have this wonderful feeling in stressful environments or during difficult times? In asking this question, we're falling once again into the trap of believing that external, outside circumstances are responsible for how we feel. And as I'm sure you're going to expect me to answer if you've stayed with me this far, there's no reason why we can't.

It's still completely possible to feel calm and centred despite complication, confusion and uncertainty in the external world. The feeling and thought connection doesn't only work in favourable conditions. It's working all the time, no exceptions. You can enjoy an expansive feeling, a certainty that all is well and tap into a quiet inner knowing, wherever you find yourself.

An incident from my life a couple of decades ago shows how it's possible to access this quality of feeling even under extreme circumstances. I lived near Manchester, a city in the north of England at the time and had ventured into the city centre for a haircut and morning spent shopping.

Whilst the hairdresser was carefully working on my precision-cut bob we suddenly heard the city centre was being evacuated in response to a bomb threat phone call. My hairdresser frantically snipped away so that I didn't have to leave with half a haircut and then like everyone I grabbed my coat and left.

Although it was years ago, I have a vivid memory of walking back to my car quickly without fuss or alarm, away from signs of trouble. Even though many people seemed unclear what to do, ignoring police directions to move away, I knew to take action. Halfway back to my car, I heard the bomb blast. But I was safely away from any danger and thankfully whilst many people were injured by flying glass, no one was killed.

Throughout the whole experience, I can remember very clearly feeling no sense of panic, just a deep sense of calmness and connection with Eckhart Tolle's "Power of Now". I can guarantee you will be able to point to experiences like this yourself – times when even under intense pressure your mind has been quiet and clear. You've known what to do and have responded without hesitation.

Or you might have felt it during an everyday event when a little more than usual was required of you. It can also show up whilst you're doing something you enjoy, a skill you've developed – playing an instrument, riding a horse or diving in the ocean. It will be there in your life somewhere and I can say this with total confidence because I know this is something we all possess.

It's there waiting patiently under whirring thoughts and a busy mind. It's not something you need to conjure up with techniques, it's about letting go and there it is. This is the beauty of unexpected consequences. Not just a lessening of stress but an accessing of something wise, clear-seeing and deep. It enables you to slow down to the present moment, to notice more and feel a greater sense of gratitude for the life you already have and the beauty there.

This isn't to say that I never get irritated, cross or moody. I still get tetchy sometimes when my daughter is taking an age to get ready for school in the mornings and I find it difficult to stay calm when I'm late (definitely my pet hate!). My moods go up and down and I still have days here and there when I feel I'd be better off staying in bed with the duvet over my head - this isn't an inoculation against an experience of all life's peaks and troughs.

But there is more.

I no longer get lost in stress and overwhelm for days and days. If I have occasional bouts they're light and pass more quickly. I no longer worry and stress about what might happen or which problems I could face in the future. Life has become lighter, more enjoyable and something to be savoured.

That for me is huge progress.

**Over to you**

Can you think of times when you've felt this feeling?

When have you been able to relax into life even when everything around you is chaotic?

# Chapter 16: Racing with The Flintstones

**In which we discover how living with this understanding creates a more relaxed way of being in the world and all of a sudden, more time.**

As this is a book about midlife, you may be old enough to remember The Flintstones, a children's TV cartoon from the sixties. I loved these stories and characters as a child. I was particularly fond of the cars – stone wheels, all the latest stone-age technology and all the drivers had to do to speed the car up was to use more effort and run faster.

Harder + more effort = success

This idea makes perfect sense to us. The more we work, the harder we try, the greater results we're going to achieve – that's how life works. Even though we hate the feelings of pressure, stress and overwhelm, it seems obvious there's a correlation, a link between struggle and getting things done. Striving hard equals achievement is pretty much a given in our culture.

When we're struggling and stressed, for many of us, what also threatens to throw us out of the light aircraft of overwhelm without a parachute is the feeling of not having enough time. We find ourselves trying to pack more and more tasks into the day and it can feel as if we're constantly trying to carve out a few extra hours. Our to-do list just keeps on getting longer and longer and because of our lack of enthusiasm and motivation, chores that should be dealt with quickly take forever. We're constantly dodging interruptions. We're easily distracted and find focus impossible as our mind whirls around.

It's exhausting and frustrating.

One of my favourite treats last year was to join a kayaking session, a perfect illustration of how much fun can come from the most unlikely of circumstances, even sitting in a confined space with a soggy bottom for hours.

When we first set off down the river, to avoid crashing into moored boats or other kayaks my steering technique involved tightening my lower back muscles and trying to heave myself around by force. It was a lot of effort and not especially successful. But as we got further towards the sea, I became distracted. I started chatting to my fellow kayakers and to relax into the experience. My back muscles unwound and softened. I steered my kayak without thought, with ease.

Like that experience, how often do we think we have to take tight control of every aspect of our life when we're trying to tackle the stress in our life? We tense against it. We don't trust our ability to be able to handle every scenario and we try too hard, way too hard. We think it's up to us, every minute detail, that any progress is in our hands and on our heads.

We fear if we don't keep it together it's all going to come crashing down upon us. This means we have to mentally keep a fix on lengthy lists of tasks and obligations and micro-manage our time. Our overthinking creates complications, foresees difficulty around every corner like some demonic fortune teller with a crystal ball of doom. Life becomes overwhelming and struggle and strain.

Yet it can be far easier than this.

There's no giant rule book of life that says it *has* to be this way. Earlier in the book, I suggested this was a subtractive psychology which means it's descriptive rather than prescriptive. It guides us gently into an understanding of *how* the human mind works and *how* we experience reality rather than providing us with a list of things to do to acquire inner peace and happiness.

I used to work really hard to find a quiet, contented mind - gratitude journals, affirmations, visualisations. I had such a long list that I barely had time for anything else. I meditated on and off for a few years. I created space in my day to slow my breathing, take my attention within, quieten my mind, and if I could, fight off niggling and repetitive thoughts. Finally, if I was lucky, the feeling of space and tranquillity that I desired would be carried through into the rest of my day.

There's no doubt I did find some comfort in all these techniques that kept me so busy. But underneath was the fundamental assumption that I had to continue to do them to find mental and emotional peace – I was broken and chaotic and constant fixing was required. How much easier to realise I have everything I already need within me, that I possess an internal guidance system I can rely on. There's such simplicity in understanding that peace of mind is already mine, that unlocking that quiet space within was never about piling on technique after technique or having more to do and think.

It's about having much less on our minds, trusting life to take care of the fiddly details and then as we lean more and more into this whole understanding, our mind becomes quieter and calmer.

There's an increase in clarity and consequently, focus.

We're still going to have goals we want to reach, things we want to do, people to go and see. Please don't fear this is going to turn you into a laid back, "can't ever be bothered with anything ever again" couch potato. There's a world of difference between being relaxed and completely giving up. But when our mind is quieter, there's less internal chatter about our ability (or lack) of achieving our goals. There's no inner debate taking place, no resistance and fear, just an awareness of the next step to take. We see the distinction between what needs to be done and what's irrelevant time-wasting like scrolling through social media, tidying a bookshelf, or dusting a table, far more clearly.

The next step is taken easily and effortlessly. With more space, fresh, new insights come to mind directing and informing the next way to look. It's an easier way to live, a slower pace. And it's not that nothing ever gets done. More gets done with less interference from a mind troubled by worry and overdoing.

I've noticed, again and again, that I find myself taking the very steps I thought would be so difficult and which previously would have involved a great deal of mental planning. analysing and rehearsing (aka overthinking). Painting the house, taking up cycling again, booking the sea kayaking day I'd longed to do for so long - even, heaven forbid, completing tax returns! It all gets done. And any sudden crisis that pops up is dealt with, at the right time, without drama, with ease and no extraneous worrying and fretting.

97

Gill Edwards referred to this as flow time in her wonderful book "Pure Bliss". We glide from one task to another and more seems to get done, faster as our experience of time shifts from busy and cluttered to relaxed and spacious.

And then all of a sudden we discover we have far more time on our hands. We even find we're sat in that never-expected-in-our- lifetime situation of twiddling our thumbs wondering what on earth to do with these extra hours. Our chores list seems to have dissolved and vanished in a puff of magical smoke. The very quality of mind we so longed for when we felt stressed is ours without grasping and grabbing for it. Time is no longer the enemy and life has inexplicably become simple and elegant, the way ahead clear and obvious instead of fighting through a mass of loud and disorganised thoughts.

So in this chapter, we've looked at how living with this understanding leads to less struggle and finding we have more time. Now I know I don't need to work as hard on mind and emotional control as I used to when I misunderstood where my experience was coming from. And for those times when I feel like I'm spinning back out of control into trying too hard, I see now how falling back into ease is merely a thought away.

By spending time studying how the mind really works, before turning back to look at my own life, I've noticed how many of the so-called problems that I spent so long trying to fix, have simply dissolved. Falling into living this easier way means that a quiet mind, gratitude, slowing down, all of these are simply by-products of integrating the certainty of the connection between my thoughts and feelings. It's all happened easily and naturally and I haven't had to work on anything.

And yes there really is less we have to do.

**Over to you**

Where are you trying too hard in your life?

What do you find easy and effortless?

How could you relax more into the flow of life?

# Chapter 17: Following the Gingerbread Crumbs Back Home

**In which we look at the advantage of allowing life to lead the way.**

Despite our best intentions, our goals and plans so much of life is unpredictable. It's impossible to anticipate sudden events or challenges that we'll face tomorrow, next week, let alone next year, despite our confidence that we live in a world that trundles sedately along a familiar path. If we think back through our life it's so often the seemingly chance encounters or the sudden changes in direction that in hindsight have a profound influence on our life.

As I finish this chapter, we're living through week three of a total UK lockdown which means for all of us, holidays booked, celebrations arranged, not to mention, daily routines have all been abruptly canceled and curtailed. I can confidently predict that at New Year celebrations, no one saw that coming.

At times like these, we can find ourselves getting stressed because life isn't living up to expectations or following the path we would have it take. We may even notice worrisome thoughts floating through our mind as we wonder how much control over our life we actually do have.

We have our plans and ambitions and of course, we can take steps towards them but it seems to me that there is also something else at play here too. Call it fate if you will or destiny but despite our best intentions, life has paths for each of us that are very often above and beyond that which we can see for ourselves. They show up in the unexpected twists of fate, the unforeseen happy co-incidences or the out of the blue opportunities (let alone the tragedies and setbacks that we never could have anticipated).

Now I'm certainly not suggesting that we just sit back and allow life to happen, that we become apathetic and let life be done to us. That's not what I'm saying. If I have a strong desire to join an expedition to the South Pole with a team of dogs, I should start training, do my research and take the steps to make it a reality. But if in the meantime, I get an invitation to join a research mission to the moon, (not sure they're taking unskilled-in-the-field, midlife women, at the moment for this one but you never know), then it makes total sense to stay open and flexible to the opportunities that life throws my way.

I know this idea that we are flotsam, drifting aimlessly with the tide, having less control than we might think over life's direction can initially sound depressing and disheartening and we might start to question why we bother. But paradoxically, it has the potential to be immensely freeing. We can allow life to flow through us, to be lived through us. We can start to trust the direction of life more fully, accept whatever is handed to us and live beyond the often narrow bandwidth of "I will only be happy if these specific factors and circumstances show up in my life."

The entire premise of this book is that external factors – the weather, tricky colleagues and health concerns are not responsible for our stress. Our stress comes from our thoughts.

That's it, full stop, the end.

And as we've already seen, our feelings provide no more information on the state of our life other than as a barometer of our thoughts. Happy thoughts, joyful feelings, sad thoughts, miserable feelings whether we're sat on a beautiful beach or stuck in a ten-mile tailback.

When we have an insightful, knowing experience of this, when we "get it", we are not only more accepting of any mood but achieving certain conditions and results in the external world becomes less compelling. If my child's rude to me over breakfast, I may correct her behaviour so that she learns how to talk to people pleasantly and get on with them but I'm not going to be trying to control her behaviour so that I can feel good about myself. Buying the expensive watch to create a happy feeling no longer seems to make sense.

We start to notice that we are more content to follow what seems to be showing up in our life. Living in this type of house, or following that sort of career path becomes less and less crucial to our emotional health. There is a feeling of openness to whatever life experiences are brought to us.

When I finally allowed myself to feel more comfortable with this idea, it brought an incredible sense of relief and peace, knowing that an intelligence greater than mine had my back. I felt I could take a deep, relaxing breath as the weight of all that expectation and striving I had for myself, just faded away. And with it, this insight took away so much of my midlife stress. I didn't need to fight life and circumstances anymore. All the "if only I'd done this or that when I was younger" thoughts or "have I got time left to do this or that?"

All of it drifted away.

That's not to say I don't still have dreams and desires. Yes, there are many things I would love to happen in my life, things I would love to have and do - adventure in frozen climates, weekends in ritzy hotels, a Scandinavian husband (apologies Mr E), longer legs (a life-long dream). I would love all of that. But what I *do* have is far more acceptance of how some of it's going to show up and work out for me exactly as I would wish it and some of it isn't. Sometimes things are meant to be in my life and sometimes they're not. So I can just sit back, relax and enjoy the journey.

Funnily enough, over time I began to notice how change invariably started showing up in my life without effort and work on my part. I stopped reacting to each small setback as if it were the greatest disappointment I'd ever had to face. Some of the wishes I'd held onto so dearly and tightly, I realised had crept into my life almost without me noticing. And I started to notice little steps forward began to crop up in my life with no seeming effort on my part. All I had to do was to pay attention, notice the signs and the whispers and then take action.

As I said earlier, this is not about never taking charge again or sitting back with a good book and box of chocolates with your feet up and doing nothing. There's a subtle difference because with a quiet mind and less stressing thinking, there's more space to notice what the next step could be and less mental resistance to taking it.

Let's take getting fit for example. Friends have often encouraged me out for runs but despite thorough and enthusiastic stretching and warming up, I seem to suffer niggling injuries too often. Frankly, I'm not really built for running and whilst I can see many people enjoy pounding around the countryside, it's an activity I loathe.

What I do love though is to swim. I love the feeling of weightlessness, and the sense of the water on my skin and I sign up once a year to complete a 5k sponsored swim which is just enough motivation to keep me swimming regularly. There's a pool close to where I live, I can easily fit it into my day and it's so much easier. I can stay fit. Look closely and we can see that life provides many, many opportunities for us to reach the same goal.

When life doesn't turn out the way I want it to there's less angst – it's all part of the greater plan. And what this means is there is never any failure to worry about. There is so much more space in my mind - space to enjoy the little joyful details of life, space to notice what needs to be done and less fretting about stress.

It's an incredibly freeing feeling.

Stress and worry feel like a way of squashing the body and spirit down into a tiny, restrictive space, it feels heavy and tight. But living with this understanding feels like expansion. It feels like standing on a cliff, opening arms wide and breathing long and deep and inhaling it all.

It's trusting in the great scheme of life.

And this doesn't mean that awful, terrible things aren't ever going to happen. They may, they will. But I now trust that they will be dealt with, whatever emotions arise, all will be well.

**Over to you**

Where has life led you in completely unexpected directions that turned out to be perfect for you?

# Chapter 18: Taking Happy Ever After With Us Wherever We Go

**In which we uncover what this has all really been about and how this can be the start of your journey into so much more.**

Right at the beginning of this book, I wanted you to know your reaction to stress is never an indication there's something wrong with you or that you need fixing in any way.

It never ever was.

It's time to say more about this. We may have spent so much of our life thinking small. But once we open our mind to living the way I've described in this book, as countless others are discovering, we realise we are far more powerful and impressive than we ever suspected we could be.

Before I left the seaside holiday I wrote about earlier, I went for an early morning swim in the harbour. It was sublime! Small clouds floated over a pale blue sky, occasional waves crashed over the sea wall and the sound of gulls shrieked through the air. Even the air tasted salty. The water was so bracingly chill and despite the passing thought that I might lose toes to frostbite, it quite took my breath away. It was wonderful and I wish you could have been there with me.

What was especially glorious about this dip was that I was fully and totally immersed in it – the feel of the cold water against my skin, the sounds, and sights and smells of it all. I was completely present in that experience – living every second of it with a quiet mind and total presence.

And life can really be that simple.

All that is ever required of us is to be fully present so that we are awake and aware. Awake to who we really are, aware of our true potential and brilliance and open and ready, for whatever life might bring. When I look back over my journey with stress and a deepening dive into this understanding, I realise it was always more than becoming comfortable with my life and my age and not getting so overwhelmed and stressed.

I still have moments when I feel lost and uncertain and frustrated that life isn't going the way I would like, but they are now mere blips. The great miracle is I have an inkling of who I really am (and who you are). There is further exploration for me to do here I know. I will never reach the end of this journey but I have a greater understanding of how much potential we all have.

This has given me a tremendous sense of peace.

I guess what I'm saying and what I hinted at earlier in the book is that this was never about simply dealing with the problem of your menopausal symptoms, your boss, or money or whatever was causing you stress and problems. It was never just about tackling overwhelm and worry.

I hope for you too it's been much wider and deeper than that. It's about ultimately discovering how glorious and magnificent we truly are, how much we have to offer the world and how much there is for us to uncover about ourselves.

I would love to know how you get on with this. If it's your first journey into this understanding and some part of this message has struck you, that's brilliant. Keep exploring. Read and discover as much as you can and you will find that more will be revealed for you in the most delightful way.

If everything you have read here makes no sense and you fear for my sanity, again I would urge you to stay with it and carry on staying in this conversation. If my words have created a smidgeon of interest for you, have a look at what others have written and said about this. There's a huge amount of free information out there and there are many, many others starting to teach this understanding.

Keep on taking each step forward.

But in the meantime, for now, I wish you an exhilarating journey and much, much love.

"Let everything happen to you

Beauty and terror

Just keep going

No feeling is final."

Rainer Maria Rilke.

**Over to you**

What has been the most important insight you've had whilst reading this book?

How has your reaction to stress changed?

How are you going to continue this journey?

# Appendix - The Three Principles

We owe our awareness of these principles to Sydney (Syd) Banks a Scottish welder who moved to Canada and in the early 1970s suddenly had an insight so profound that people who knew him, reported it permanently transformed him.

What's so deliciously perfect about Syd is that he wasn't your normal guru-guy material. He wasn't well-read (in fact he admitted himself that he barely read books and his education had been minimal). He didn't have years and years of meditation experience, nor had he ever studied ancient texts or spent time traveling through India searching for spiritual teachers.

I'm sure had he done all these things, we'd feel compelled to follow his example, book those travel tickets and visit those spiritual libraries.

Thank heavens he hadn't.

Rather, his story demonstrates that enlightenment and access to these truths are available to anyone, not just the "I'm more evolved than you" few. It's not necessary to jump through spiritual hoops to raise our vibrational level to access them; they are but an insight or fresh thought away. And that's true for all of us.

**So what sparked this understanding for Sydney?**

He'd been attending a relationship course with his wife and during a conversation with a psychologist, Syd had been talking about his lack of confidence. The psychologist replied "You don't lack confidence, you only think you do." an innocent enough sounding remark (we're probably heard this ourselves many times), but Syd heard this very differently on this occasion.

Unexpectedly, it spun him into a sudden insight that led to what's become known as The Three Principles – Mind, Consciousness and Thought (or the Inside Out Understanding) which together explain how we create our experience of life and who and what we really are.

**The Principle of Mind – we are connected to all life and there's a greater intelligence working beyond it all.**

Whatever our religious or spiritual views, there's no denying there's an energy or quality to life. Different cultures and people have different names for this ranging from God, Life Source to Universal Energy.

It's the infinite space from which everything originates and the intelligence behind it all that determines whether a seed grows into a blade of grass or a daisy. We too are formed from it and so this principle means we're always connected to a deep intelligence and wisdom (whether we're aware of it or not).

**The Principle of Consciousness – we're aware**

Consciousness enables us to be aware of being alive, of being in the world and of recognising that we're having experiences, sensations, thoughts and feelings. Coupled with the next principle, it gives us the potential for understanding where our experience comes from so we need never be the victim of our circumstances.

## The Principle of Thought – we think

Thought is the mental activity that flows through us- always there, continually changing. This principle isn't referring to any specific thoughts we might have but our potential for any form of mental activity and creation, it's pointing to the fact *that* we think.

Together The Three Principles create our human experience and one of the best ways I have heard the interplay between them described is as it's like being in a giant cinema - Mind is the projector, Consciousness the screen and Thought the film being projected onto the screen.

"Whoopy-do!" You may well be thinking at this point! Or, "yes, but how does this help?"

At a fundamental level, what these Principles mean is that we are part of something greater than ourselves and that our experience of life, the good, the bad and the ugly, comes from Thought, from the Inside Out.

What I have shared in this book are the implications of those Principles for us, living our lives on a day to day basis. As time moves on, as I have more insights, I will see more and more about them and if you allow their significance to seep into you, I promise you, so will you.

# A Few Words About Tumaini Childrens Charity

**Proceeds from the sale of each book will go to the Tumaini Childrens Charity in support of the fabulous work they do for children in Kenya.**

Hannah has a huge heart and is one of the most generous spirits I have ever met (I know she's going to hate me writing this but it's the truth) and she has worked tirelessly for this charity over the past couple of decades.

When I saw her emotional Facebook live explaining how they were running out of money for food for the children in her charity, I was blubbing within minutes, and going on the sudden influx of donations, so were many other people.

I recently read somewhere that when we're in a difficult situation or struggling in some way, it's an invitation to let go of some small part of ourselves and embrace something more expansive. Certainly, this was my experience of dealing with my own stress and it was Hannah's when she followed her inspiration to reach out for help.

When I wrote this book and shared my idea with Hannah of giving the proceeds to Tumaini, it was no longer about me selling a book, it became about us.

I'm sorry that you've struggled with stress and that's why you bought this book but already by paying the money to feed a child, you're part of a wider community, you're part of something bigger.

Thank you so much for taking that step and I hope you find the answers you seek.

## A message from Hannah Ellis – Tumaini chairperson

They say there are 330 million children in the world not able to access basic numeracy and literacy skills. They say education breaks the cycle of poverty. They say that all children have the right to education regardless of race or disability, that they have the right to be protected from exploitation and be free from emotional, physical abuse and neglect. They say they have a right to be loved.

When I was a girl, I used to think the world was run by "goodies" who would discover the broken parts and then fight to fix them. Then I discovered too often it is those in charge who allow children to be vulnerable, unloved and uneducated. It's down to you and me to choose to fight for children to have at least one meal a day, to receive an education and to know they are valued.

In Kenya, Tumaini is the place where I have had the privilege of playing a part in rescuing thousands of vulnerable children. It is a place called Hope because it is where children can approach problems with a mindset for success.

The money you paid for this book will pay for a child to be fed for a couple of weeks.  So thank you so much for being one of the "goodies" who enabled the rights of a child to be met today.

**To find out more visit tumainichildrenscharity.org**

# Notes

**Chapter Six**

Kelly McGonigal, The Upside of Stress (Vermilion, 2015).

**Chapter Eight**

A.A. Milne, Winnie-The-Pooh (Methuen Children's Books, 1973)

**Chapter Nine**

Martin E.P.Seligman, Learned Optimism (1990, Simon and Schuster Inc)

**Chapter Thirteen**

Gill Edwards. Living Magically (1991, Piatkus)

**Chapter Sixteen**

Gill Edwards, Pure Bliss (1999, Piatkus)

# Acknowledgements

There are so many of you who have helped and guided me along the way and I want you to know how grateful I am to you all.

To Alison Dunevein-Gordon, Sally Holland and Jennie Blakehill. Thanks for your encouragement and for all your guidance and support in our monthly meetings. I can't tell you how invaluable those sessions were.

Hannah Ellis, Jules Stott Morgan and Louise Mackenzie my Cherhill lovelies. Heartfelt thanks for wonderful conversations, lovely feedback of one of my (many) early drafts of this book and for general cheering on duties.

Many thanks to Rudi and Jules Kennard, my huge-hearted, loving inspirations. Thank you so much for helping me see so much more and for being so supportive and generous. Also big hugs and thanks to all the other Innate Evolution practitioners. What an amazing time we've had together!

Nicola Bird of A Little Peace of Mind and to the wonderful Little Peace of Mind mentors. Thank-you, Nic for setting up the mentor programme which was so important for giving me the confidence to start sharing the Three Principles. Thanks as well to my fellow mentors for your generous feedback on my manuscript and for all your supportive and helpful suggestions.

Thanks to Jenny Anderson and Dave Elleray of Freedom Thinking for your amazing retreat which turned out to be such an important introduction to this understanding for me.

To all those teachers and mentors I haven't met but who have taught me so much. Sydney Banks, Michael Neill, whose on-line programmes have been so important to me. Jamie Smart – thanks for the Clarity Pro membership, it was such a great help. Deb and Becs of Dare to BU, Mary Schiller, Clare Dimond, Elsie Spittle, Dicken Bettinger, George Pransky and Jacquie Forde.

To my Mother, Emma Robinson, Tracey Swainson and Leonora Mason for just being there with me!

And finally, thank-you Jeni Braund for starting me off on this journey all those decades ago.

# A Final Request

In the time it's taken you to read this book, another 456,666 (maybe slightly less) books have been published on Amazon.

If you have found this book moderately helpful/ loved it/ best book ever, I'd be really grateful if you would leave me a review there to prevent it from being squashed. unloved and forgotten amongst all the other titles.

Many, many thanks.

# About the Author

Dawn Robinson is a workshop leader and a coach for midlife women. She spent over one and a half decades slogging away in organisations in HR and as a management trainer and then a number of years floating around as an Alexander Technique teacher helping people use their bodies with more ease and less strain.

Dawn lives in the UK with her husband and daughter. When she's not working she is often roaming the countryside armed with a map, a flask of tea and a large slab of cake (and trying to avoid lightning strikes).

**FREE Book bonuses**

If you would like access to a workbook with all the "over to you" questions along with additional audios and videos, sign up for your free book bonus materials using this address. **www.theflourishing-midlife.com/book-extras**

I look forward to seeing you there!

Made in the USA
Middletown, DE
28 September 2020